Severe and Hazardous Weather

An Introduction to High Impact Meteorology

Active Learning Exercises

6th Edition

Robert M. Rauber

John E. Walsh

Donna J. Charlevoix

Cover Image: Shutterstock.com

Images not credited are by Robert M. Rauber

Kendall Hunt
publishing company

www.kendallhunt.com
Send all inquiries to:
4050 Westmark Drive
Dubuque, IA 52004-1840

ISBN 978-1-7924-6283-2

Published in the United States of America

Contents

Preface

These *Active Learning Exercises* that accompany *Severe and Hazardous Weather* were developed for in-classroom use to reinforce concepts. Most exercises can be completed in about ten minutes. In our classes, students complete an exercise right after the material is taught or we assign the activity as homework to review key concepts.

Bob Rauber
r-rauber@illinois.edu

John Walsh
j-walsh2@illinois.edu

Donna Charlevoix
charlevo@gmail.com

Name: ______________________________ Class: ___________Date: _________

Exercise 1.1 – Geography Overview

Understanding where severe weather is developing or has occurred it a key part of studying hazardous events. Test your knowledge of geography by completing the questions below.

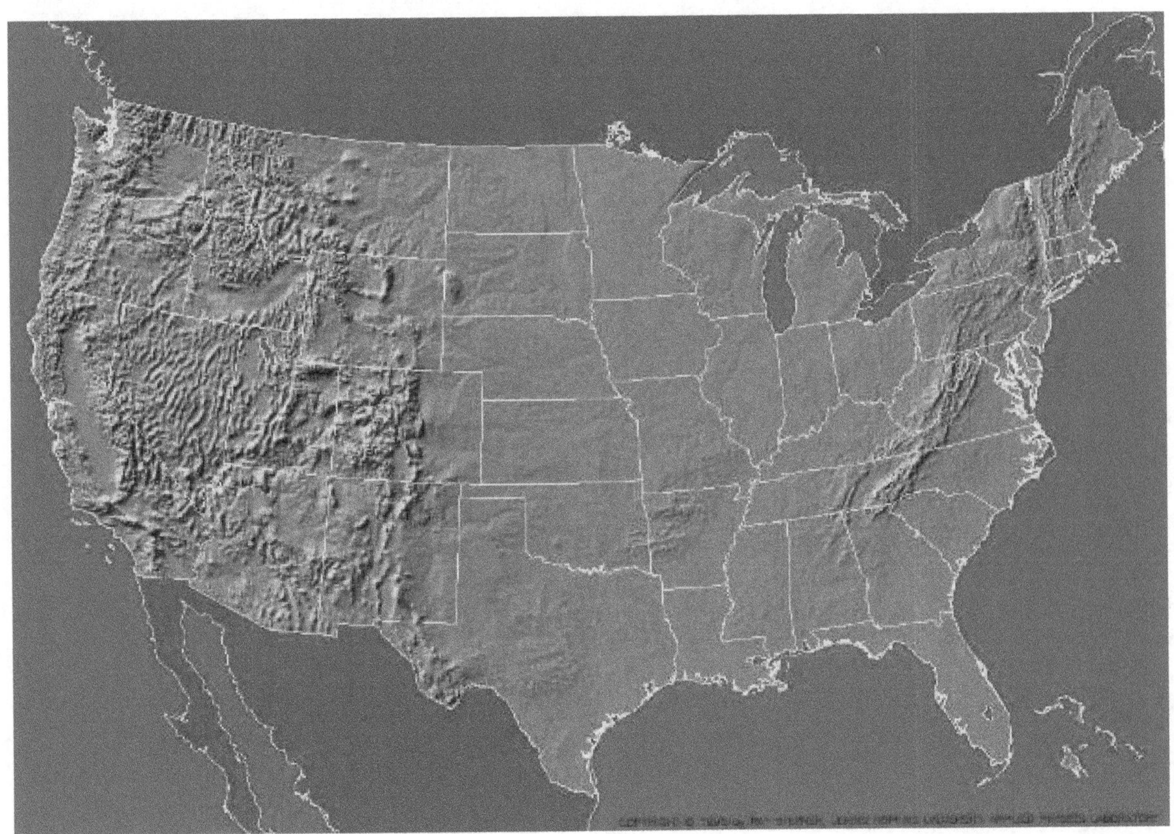

1. Identify major mountain ranges by drawing a line along the crest of the mountains and label each line: Rocky Mountains (Rockies), Sierra Nevada (Sierra), Cascade Range (Cascades), Appalachian Mountains (Appalachians), and Coastal Range (Coastal).
2. Label the Atlantic Coastal Plain (ACP) and the Great Plains (GP).
3. Label the Great Lakes: Huron, Ontario, Michigan, Erie, Superior.
4. Label the Pacific Ocean (PO), the Atlantic Ocean (AO), and the Gulf of Mexico (GoM).
5. Identify the following states: Florida (FL), North Dakota (ND), South Carolina (SC), New York (NY), Nevada (NV), Mississippi (MS), Rhode Island (RI), Oklahoma (OK), Texas (TX), Oregon (OR) and Wisconsin (WI).
6. Identify and label the countries that neighbor the United States.

Name: ______________________________ Class: ___________ Date: __________

Exercise 1.2 – Atmospheric Temperature

As a birthday gift you receive a mercury thermometer from your long-lost Aunt who has been living in Europe for the past 20 years. As such, the units are in Celsius. Convert the temperatures to degrees Fahrenheit so you and your friends can use it more easily.

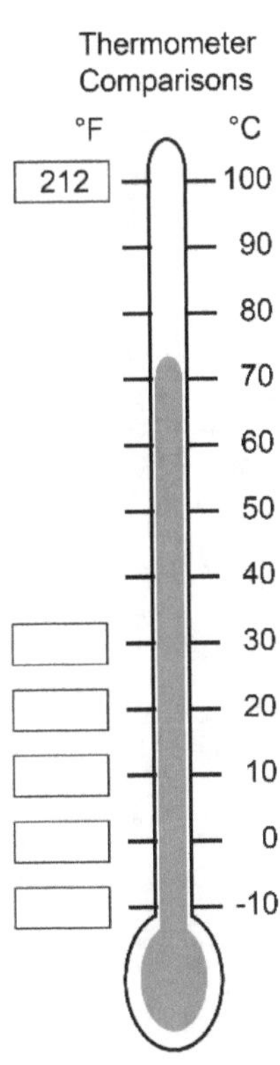

Match the severe weather events with the range of temperatures your thermometer would indicate during these storms.

Temperature Range

-20°C to -30°C
0 to -10°C
~0°C
20°C to 30°C
30°C to 40°C

(a) ___________ Nor'easter in New York City

(b) ___________ Heat waves (extreme heat) in Arizona

(c) ___________ Cold wave (extreme cold) in Montana

(d) ___________ Temperature range during severe thunderstorms in Wisconsin during July

(e) ___________ Freezing rain event in Tennessee

Name: ______________________________ Class: ___________ Date: _________

Exercise 1.3 – Atmospheric Moisture

The following air temperature (T) and dewpoint temperature (T_d) values were reported at cities across the United States in late spring. Using this data, which city has the...

	Madison, WI	Miami, FL	San Diego, CA	Fargo, ND	Lincoln, NE
T	55	83	87	40	68
T_d	37	75	51	38	50

(a) ...highest air temperature? ______________________

(b) ...highest dewpoint temperature? ______________________

(c) ...highest saturation vapor pressure? ______________________

(d) ...highest vapor pressure? ______________________

(e) ...highest relative humidity? ______________________

(f) ...lowest temperature? ______________________

(g) ...lowest dewpoint temperature? ______________________

(h) ...lowest saturation vapor pressure? ______________________

(i) ...lowest vapor pressure? ______________________

(j) ...lowest relative humidity? ______________________

(k) Saturation vapor pressure is a function of (related to) which weather variable?

____

(l) Vapor pressure is a function of (related to) which weather variable?

____

(m) How can the city with a high relative humidity have so little moisture in the air?

____

Name: ______________________________ Class: ___________Date: __________

Exercise 1.4 – Latent Heat

Phase changes of water (conversions between ice, liquid water, and water vapor) occur constantly in Earth's atmosphere. Heat is either released into the atmosphere (heating the air) or extracted from the atmosphere (cooling the air) during phase changes. In the exercises below insert the appropriate letters to indicate the correct phase change and whether the atmosphere would be heated or cooled as a result of the phase change.

	V (vapor) L (liquid) I (ice)	V (vapor) L (liquid) I (ice)	H (heating) C (cooling)

1. During *evaporation*: _____ converts to _____ which leads to _____ of the air.

2. During *melting*: _____ converts to _____ which leads to _____ of the air.

3. During *condensation*: _____ converts to _____ which leads to _____ of the air.

4. During *deposition*: _____ converts to _____ which leads to _____ of the air.

5. During *sublimation*: _____ converts to _____ which leads to _____ of the air.

6. During *freezing*: _____ converts to _____ which leads to _____ of the air.

7. Which of the six processes listed above releases the largest amount of heat to the atmosphere?

8. Which of the six processes extracts the most heat from the atmosphere?

9. What types of particles are clouds composed of?

10. What phase changes can occur during cloud formation?

11. During cloud formation, do changes of phase warm or cool the surrounding atmosphere? Why?

Name: ______________________________ Class: ____________Date: __________

Exercise 2.1 – Time Conversions

Understanding time conversion is critical to reading weather maps and forecasts. Recall that there are many ways to describe Universal Coordinated Time (UTC) including Greenwich Mean Time (GMT) and Zulu (Z).

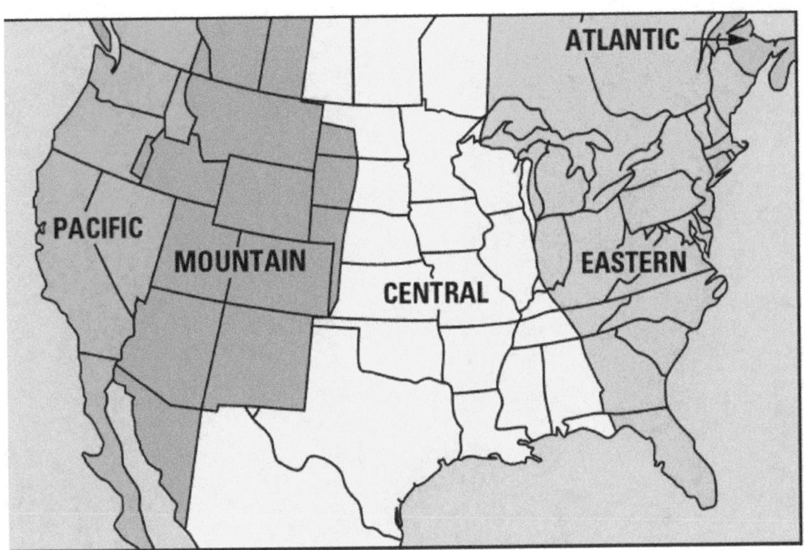

1. Fill in the table by identifying the time difference between UTC and each of the time zones. (Pacific Standard Time is completed for you (-8 hr.).)

Time Zone	Pacific Time		Mountain Time	Central Time	Eastern Time
Time Difference	Standard (PST) Daylight (PDT)	*-8 hr.*	Standard (MST) Daylight (MDT)	Standard (CST) Daylight (CDT)	Standard (EST) Daylight (EDT)

Convert the times listed below. Express you answer with a.m., p.m., noon or midnight; include the day.

2. 11 UTC, Sunday _________ Sacramento, CA (Standard)

3. 00 UTC, Saturday _________ Santa Fe, NM (Standard)

4. 18 UTC, Monday _________ Chicago, IL (Daylight)

5. 04 UTC, Friday _________ Raleigh, NC (Daylight)

6. Tuesday, 5 A.M., Orlando, FL (Daylight) _________UTC

7. Saturday, 5 P.M., Portland, OR (Standard) _________UTC

8. Thursday, 8 A.M., New York, NY (Standard) _________UTC

Name: ______________________________ Class: ____________Date: __________

Exercise 2.2 – Interpreting a Sounding

Use the data from the sounding to answer the questions. Include units when appropriate.

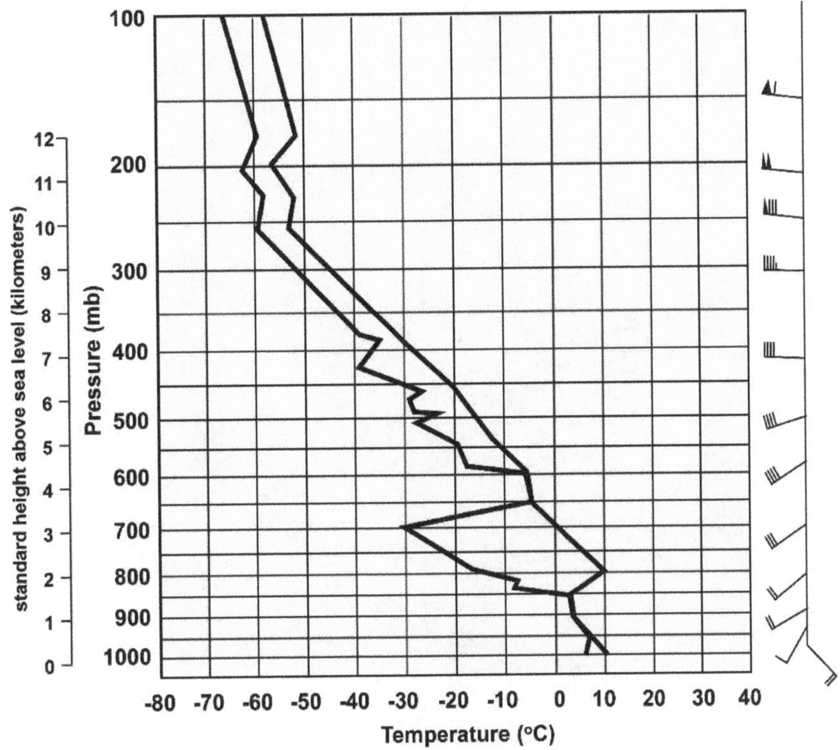

1. Identify and label the temperature line and dewpoint line on the sounding.
2. What is the 700 mb temperature? ______________
3. What is the surface pressure? ______________
4. What is the 650 mb dewpoint temperature? ______________
5. What is the 600 mb dewpoint depression? ______________
6. At what pressure level is the tropopause? ______________
7. What is the speed of the strongest wind? ______________
8. Which layers are cloud layers? (Identify the layers by the pressures at the top and bottom.)

   ______________________ and ______________________.

9. What is the wind speed and direction at 500 mb? ______________
10. Carefully circle the inversion layer in the lower atmosphere.

Name: ______________________________ Class: ___________Date: _________

Exercise 2.3 – Instruments Used for Weather Observations

Select from the list provided at least one instrument that can measure the weather information for each question. Some statements may have more than one correct answer.

Instruments

ASOS	*Doppler radar*	*Satellite*
Rawinsonde	*NLDN*	

1. Fog is present. ____________________
2. Visibility is 15 miles. ____________________
3. A thunderstorm is approaching. ____________________
4. Surface air temperature is 25°C. ____________________
5. The sea level pressure is 1013.25 mb. ____________________
6. Lightning was detected 15 miles away. ____________________
7. The wind speed at 700 mb is 20 knots. ____________________
8. One-hour rainfall accumulation is 0.75 inches. ____________________
9. An approaching thunderstorm has rotation. ____________________
10. The dewpoint depression at 500 mb is 15°C. ____________________
11. A hurricane is 400 miles south of Louisiana. ____________________
12. The dewpoint temperature at 100 mb is -40°C. ____________________
13. Large hail is falling from a severe thunderstorm. ____________________
14. The base of clouds (cloud ceiling) is at 500 meters. ____________________
15. The height of the 850 mb pressure surface is 1500 meters. ____________________
16. The temperature of the top of the highest cloud is -20°C. ____________________
17. The wind 6 km above the ground is 100 knots from the south. ____________________

Name: ______________________________ Class: ___________ Date: _________

Exercise 2.4 – Satellite and Radar Observations

Match the observational information in each question with the *best* source of information.

Source of information:

Radar reflectivity (RR)
Radar radial velocity (RV)

Visible satellite image (VIS)
Infrared satellite image (IR)
Water vapor satellite image (WV)

Observational information:

1. _______ It is about to start raining.

2. _______ Fog is along a nearby interstate highway at noon.

3. _______ Rain is falling at a rate of 3 cm/hr at your location.

4. _______ Low stratus clouds are present in the area to your west.

5. _______ Lake Michigan is warmer than the surrounding land area.

6. _______ Precipitation in a thunderstorm to your west is decreasing in intensity.

7. _______ More than 3 inches of rain fell at your location in the past 12 hours.

8. _______ A band of altostratus clouds is approaching your location at midnight.

9. _______ Your location is snow-free, but snow covers the ground 150 miles to the north.

10. _______ There is rotation in a thunderstorm approximately 30 miles to the south of your location.

11. _______ Dry air in the middle troposphere extends from Idaho to Michigan in a band approximately 300 miles wide.

Name: ______________________________ Class: ___________Date: _________

Exercise 3.1 – Decoding Surface Observations

1. Decode the surface stations; be sure to include units when appropriate.

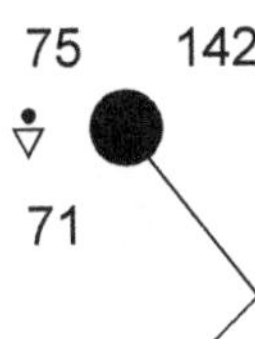

28 000

26

temperature	________	temperature	________
dewpoint temperature	________	dewpoint temperature	________
cloud cover	________	cloud cover	________
wind direction	________	wind direction	________
wind speed	________	wind speed	________
pressure	________	pressure	________
significant weather	________	significant weather	________

2. Plot surface station models for the data given. Include units when appropriate.

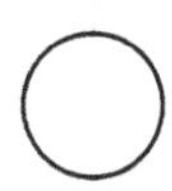

temperature = 45°F

dewpoint temperature = 45°F

cloud cover = clear

wind direction = west

wind speed = 10 kts

pressure = 1018.2 mb

significant weather = none

temperature = 31°F

dewpoint = 25°F

cloud cover = obscured

wind direction = south

wind speed = 20 kts

pressure = 999.7 mb

significant weather = heavy snow

Name: ______________________________ Class: ___________ Date: _________

Exercise 3.2 – Decoding Upper Air Observations

1. Decode the upper air (500 mb) station models. Include units when appropriate.

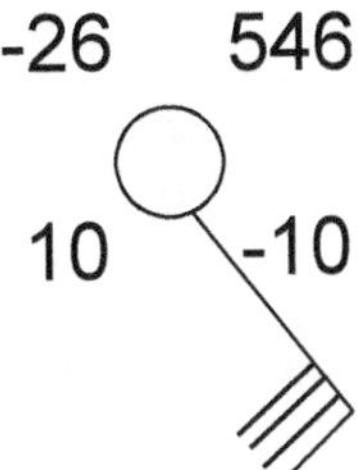

temperature ________

dewpoint depression ________

dewpoint temperature ________

wind direction ________

wind speed ________

height ________

height change ________

-15 558

5

temperature ________

dewpoint depression ________

dewpoint temperature ________

wind direction ________

wind speed ________

height ________

height change ________

2. Plot the 500 mb station models for the data given. Include units when appropriate.

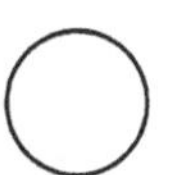

temperature =-31°C

dewpoint depression = 11

dewpoint temperature =-20°C

wind direction = south

wind speed = 70 kts

height = 5500 m

height change +500 m

temperature = –21°C

dewpoint depression = 15

dewpoint temperature = -36°C

wind direction = west

wind speed = 50 kts

height = 5520 m

height change = +200 m

Name: ______________________________ Class: ____________Date: __________

Exercise 3.3 – Contouring Weather Maps

Rules for Contouring

- Contour lines are drawn to identify constant values of an atmospheric variable.
- A contour is drawn through the station location only if the data for that station has the exact value of the contour; otherwise the contour is drawn between stations.
- Higher values are on one side of the contour and lower values on the other side.
- Contours never cross or touch each other.
- More than one contour of a given value may appear on a given map.
- All contour lines must be clearly labeled.
- Contours always form closed loops on world maps.
- Contours are drawn at equal increments of the contoured variable. Typically at intervals of: 5 or 10 °F(°C) for *isotherms* (temperature) and *isodrosotherms* (dewpoint temperature), 4 mb for *isobars* (pressure) and 5 kts for *isotachs* (wind speed).

Shown below is a map of the southeastern United States with temperatures reported at a number of stations. Contour the map at 5 degree intervals starting at 40°F

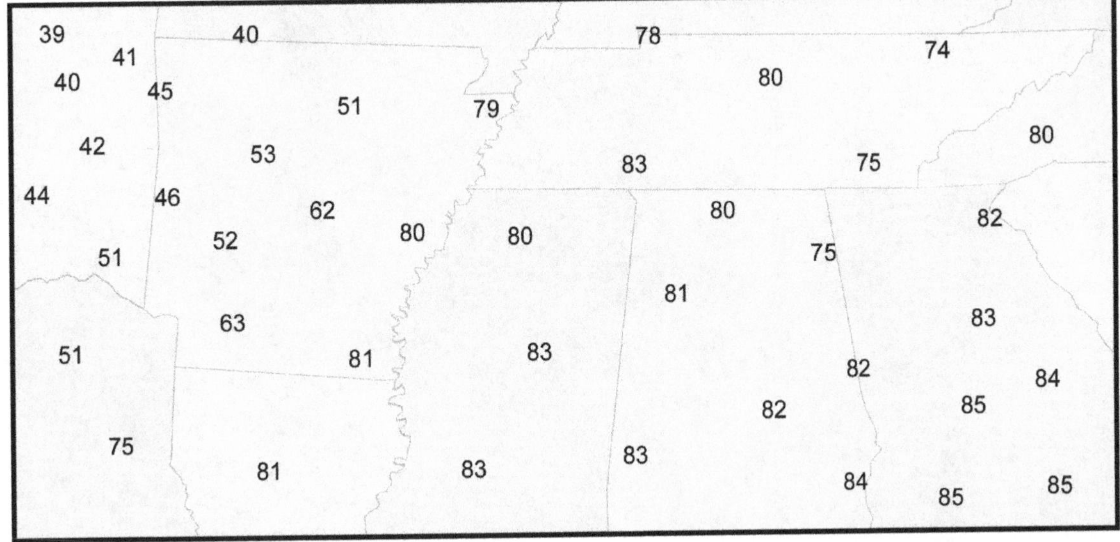

Name: ______________________________ Class: ___________Date: _________

Exercise 3.4 – Understanding Constant Pressure Charts

The map below depicts the conditions at 300 mb.

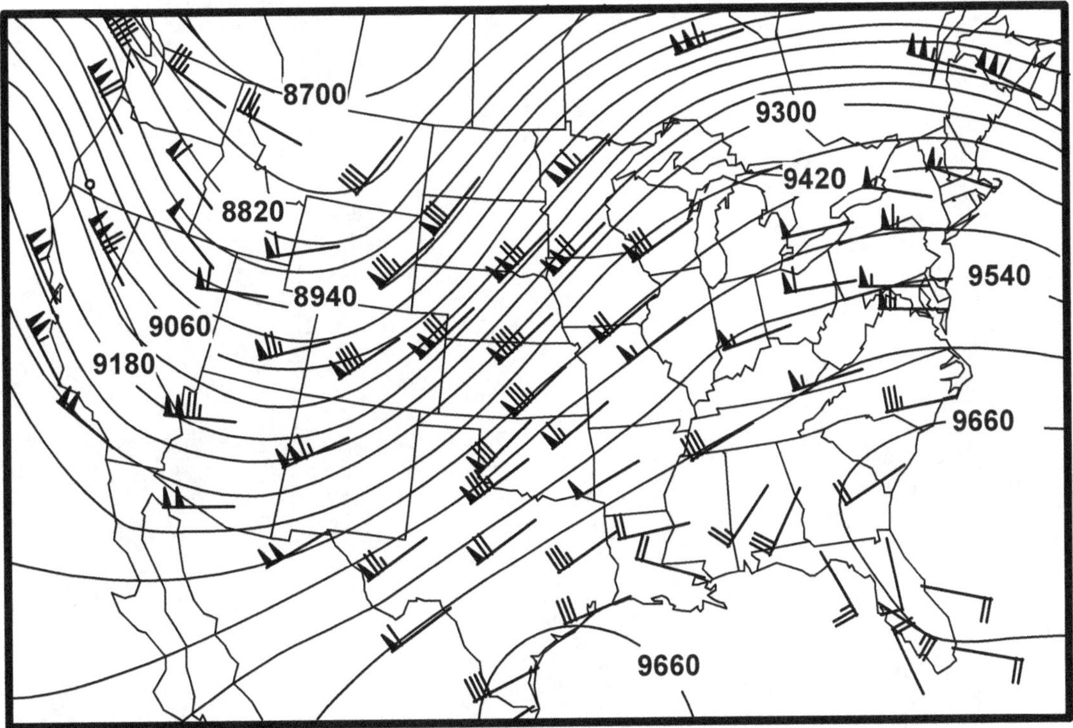

1. Draw a solid line to show the axis of the large trough over the western United States.

2. Draw a dashed line to show the axis of the large ridge over the eastern United States.

3. Draw two 100 knot isotachs (lines of constant wind speed).

4. Draw a line along the axis of the 300 mb jetstream.

5. Place an "H" in the two locations where the 300 mb surface is at its highest altitude.

6. Place an "L" in the location where the 300 mb surface is at its lowest altitude.

7. Based on this map, what can you say about the relationship between the direction and speed of the wind and the orientation and spacing of the height contours?

Name:

Name: ______________________ Class: __________ Date: __________

Exercise 3.5 – Slope of Pressure Surfaces

1. Plot the approximate altitude of each pressure surface (table below) on the vertical line above each location on the graph. Connect the points for each pressure surface.
2. Plot the altitude of the phenomena listed in the table on the vertical line to the right of the diagram.

Mt. Everest	8,800 m	Sketch the mountain
Commercial aircraft flight	10,500 m	Draw an airplane
Base of cumulus cloud	1,000 m	Sketch a cloud

3. The pressure surfaces slope toward lower altitudes in which direction? __________
4. Based on the slope of the pressure surfaces, would the temperature in North Dakota be warmer or colder than the temperature in Texas? Why?

____

	Approximate Altitude (m)		
	Southern Texas	Nebraska	North Dakota
850 mb	1,540	1,500	1,480
700 mb	3,200	3,100	2,900
500 mb	5,500	5,400	5,200
300 mb	9,800	9,500	9,200
250 mb	11,000	10,600	10,300
200 mb	12,500	12,000	11,500

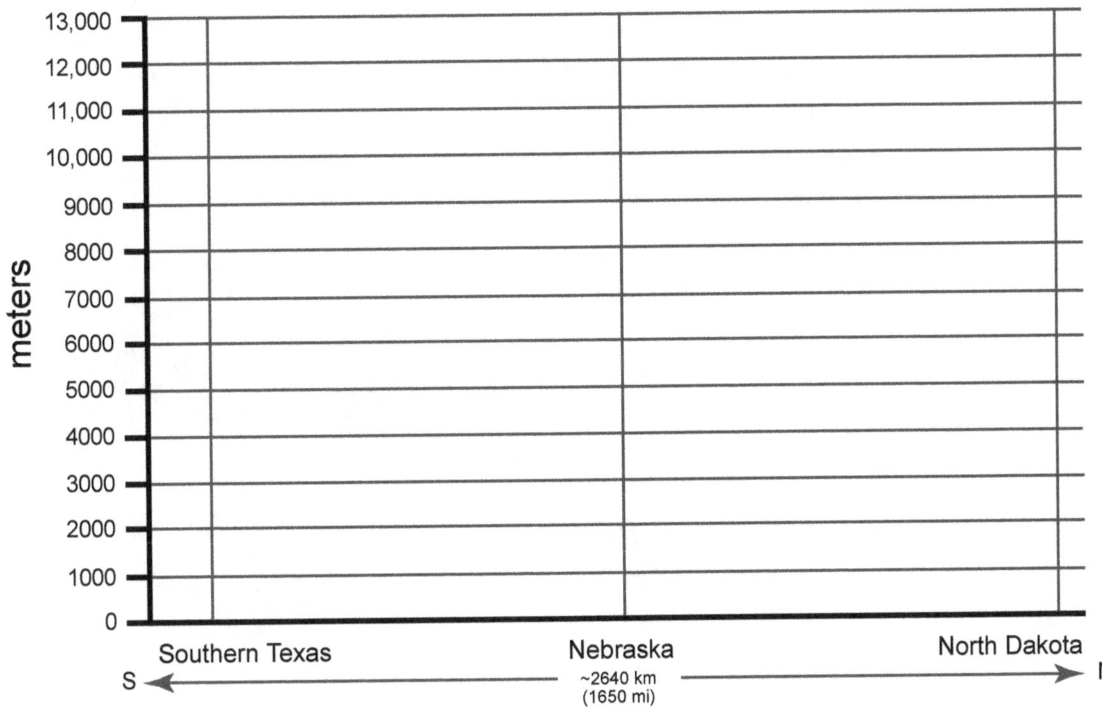

Name: ______________________________ Class: ____________ Date: __________

Exercise 4.1 – Resolution of Numerical Model Grids

In a numerical model, the number of gridpoints determines how well a weather phenomenon is resolved. Using the guide below, determine the resolution of each weather phenomenon by (a) drawing a box that estimates its size in the location indicated, (b) listing the number of gridpoints across the shortest dimension, and (c) writing the letter representing how well it is resolved. Grid points are 50 km apart.

8 or more gridpoints	→ well-resolved (W)
5 to 7 gridpoints	→ resolved (R)
2 to 4 gridpoints	→ poorly resolved (P)
less than 2	→ unresolved (U)

Phenomenon	*Size*	*# grid points*	*Resolvable?*
1. Tornado (OK)	200m × 200m	______	______
2. Sea breeze (FL)	20km × 200km	______	______
3. Thunderstorm (OK)	20km × 20km	______	______
4. Hurricane (TX Gulf Coast)	300km × 300km	______	______
5. Extratropical Cyclone (N Plains)	1500km × 1500km	______	______
6. Freezing rain band (TN)	50km × 300km	______	______
7. Cold front cloud band (PA to SC)	200km × 1000km	______	______
8. Lake-effect snow band (Lake MI)	20km × 200km	______	______

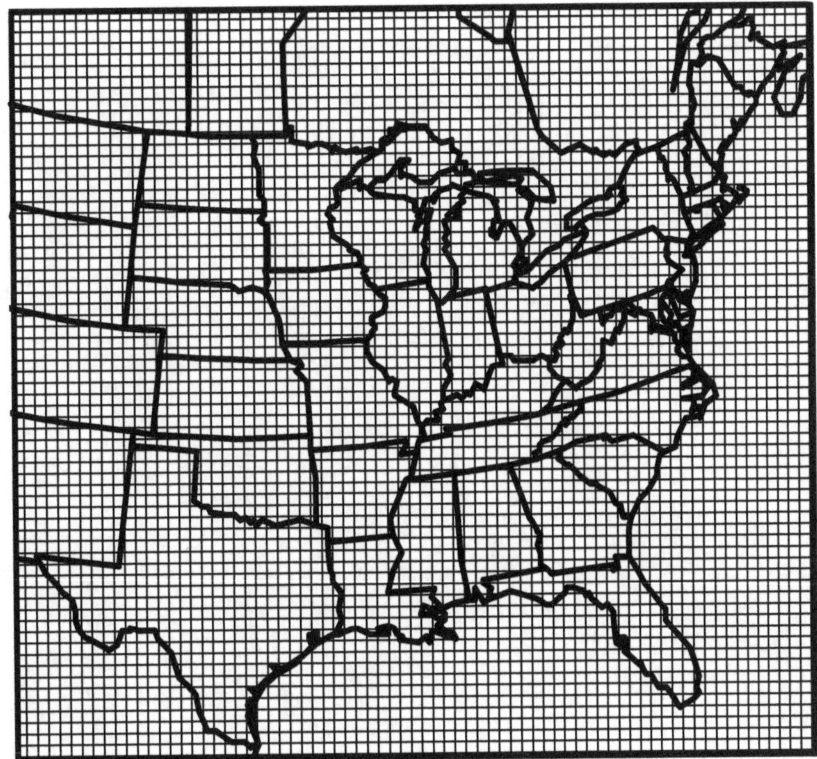

Name: ______________________________ Class: ___________ Date: __________

Exercise 4.2 – Accuracy of a Numerical Model Forecast

The top maps show a 72-hour forecast of (left) sea level pressure (isobars in black), temperature (F, colors) and winds (kts), and (right) 500 mb height (contours in black), temperature (C, colors) and winds (kts) from the GFS model run. The bottom map is the analysis of the same variables at 1200 UTC, April 12, 2021, the verification time. Evaluate the forecast by answering the questions below. All maps are valid 1200 UTC Monday April 12, 2021

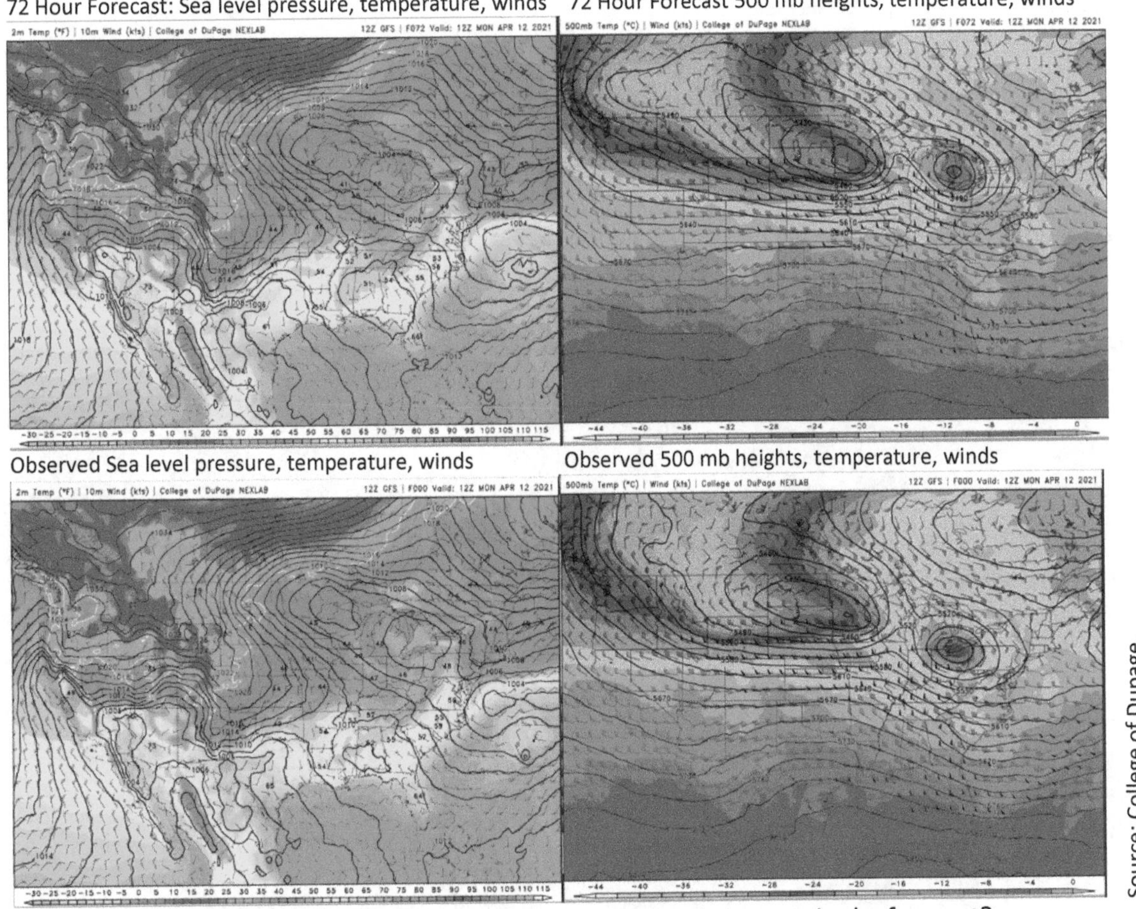

Source: College of Dupage.

1. Is the location of the low pressure system over Wisconsin correct in the forecast?

2. What is the difference in temperature in central Pennsylvania between the forecast temperature and the actual temperature?

3. What is the difference in temperature in south-central Texas between the forecast temperature and the actual temperature?

4. What is the difference in the height of the 500 mb surface over northern Ohio between the forecast and the analysis?

5. Overall, was this a good forecast?

Name: ______________________________ Class: ___________Date: __________

Exercise 4.3 – Model Resolution and Topography

The diagrams below show the same mountain range with horizontal grids superimposed. The top grid has three times the horizontal resolution of the bottom grid.

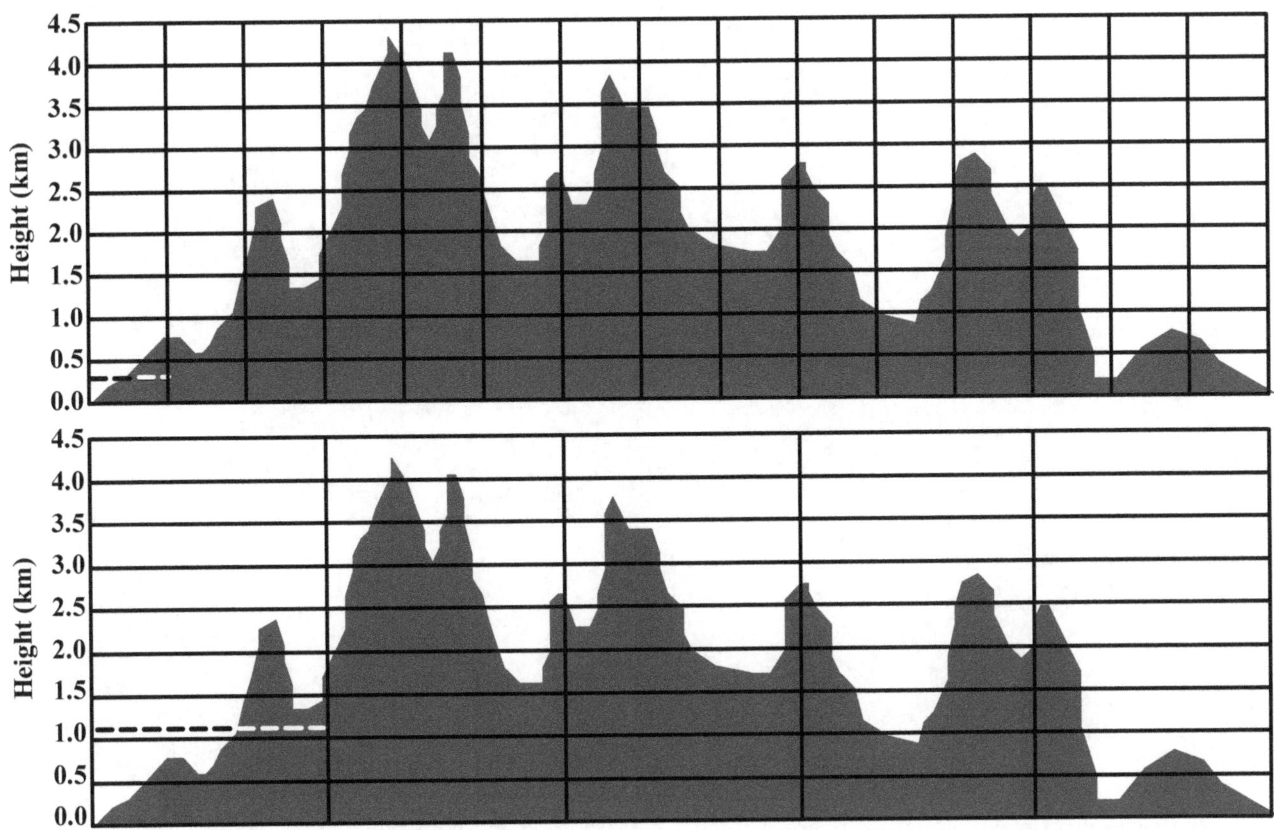

1. Draw horizontal lines to show the "average" mountain height in each grid column. The first columns are done for you (see dashed lines).

2. If air flows from left to right, on which grid would air have to rise the most to transit across the mountains? (Circle one)

   Top grid (with higher resolution) Bottom grid (with lower resolution)

3. The amount of snow that falls in mountainous areas during winter storms is closely related to the distance that air must be lifted to cross the mountains. Discuss whether you would expect higher forecast accuracy on precipitation forecasts with a higher or lower resolution grid.

Name: ______________________________ Class: ___________Date: _________

Exercise 5.1 – Seasonal Temperature Variations

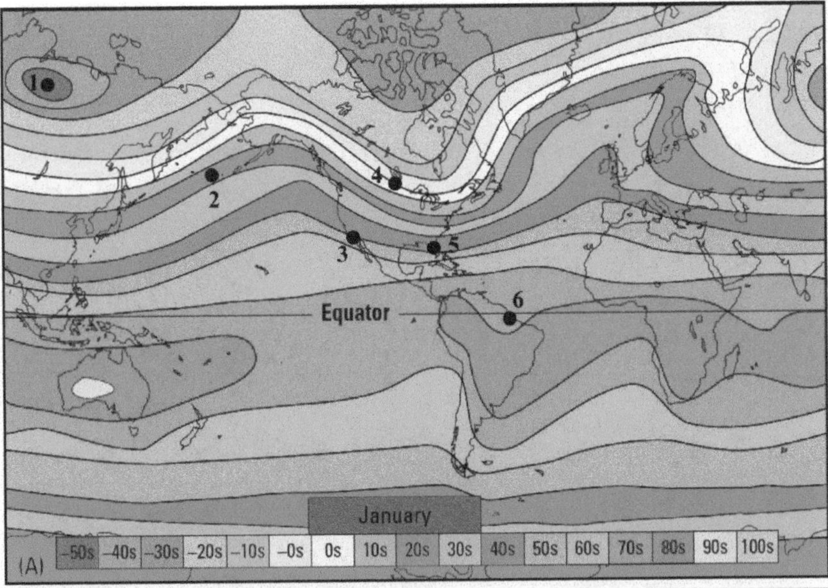

The warmest temperatures in January are in the 90s over Australia.

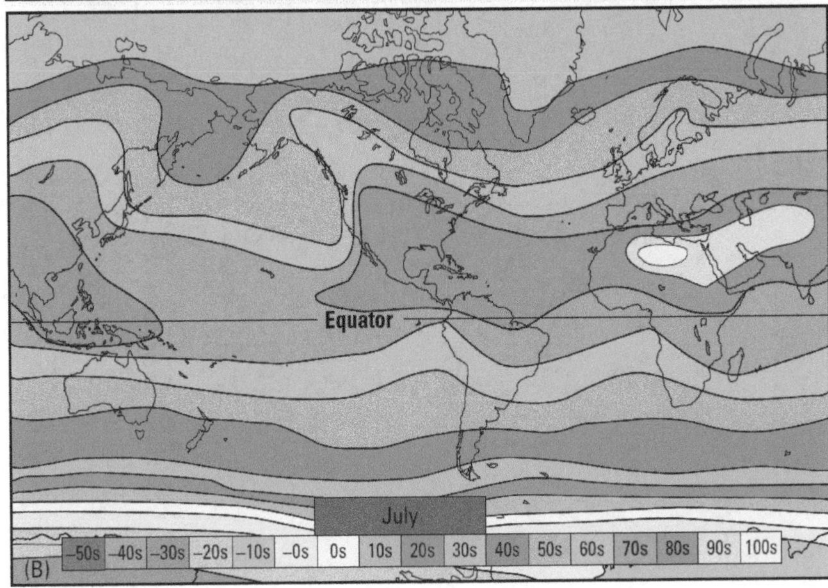

The warmest temperatures in July are in the 100s over Northern Africa.

The maps above show average January and July global temperatures. Estimate the average seasonal temperature change in degrees Fahrenheit at the following locations:

1. Northern Siberia ___________ 2. The Aleutian Islands ___________

3. Los Angeles, CA ___________ 4. Regina, Canada ___________

5. Miami, Florida ___________ 6. Amazon River Delta ___________

7. Over the globe, at what latitudes are the smallest seasonal temperature changes found?

8. Where is large seasonal temperature change found?

Name: ______________________________ Class: ___________Date: _________

Exercise 5.2 – The Earth's Orbital Parameters and Climate

The earth-sun distance is shortest in early January and largest in early July. The difference is about 3 percent. If, instead, the earth-sun distance were the same in all months (requiring that the earth's orbit around the sun be circular rather than elliptical), how would the summer and winter temperatures be different from what they are today? (Circle the correct answers.)

1a. The average summer temperature in the United States would be: hotter cooler no change

1b. The average summer temperature at Australia would be: hotter cooler no change

1c. The average winter temperature in the United States would be: warmer colder no change

1d. The average winter temperature in Australia would be: warmer colder no change

1e. Explain your answers:

Earth's axis is presently tilted about 23.5° from the plane perpendicular to the earth-sun line. If the tilt were decreased to 11.6° (about half its present value), then:

2a. The average summer temperature in the United States would be: hotter cooler no change

2b. The average summer temperature at Australia would be: hotter cooler no change

2c. The average winter temperature in the United States would be: warmer colder no change

2d. The average winter temperature in Australia would be: warmer colder no change

2e. Explain your answers:

3. Cooler summers favor the growth of ice sheets because the previous winter's snow accumulation is then less likely to melt during the summer. Which changes in the earth's orbital parameters described above would favor the growth of ice sheets in the Northern Hemisphere?

Name: ________________________________ Class: ____________ Date: __________

Exercise 5.3 – Carbon Dioxide Concentrations in the Atmosphere

The graph shows the concentrations of carbon dioxide (in parts per million by volume, ppmv) measured in the atmosphere at Mauna Loa, Hawaii. These concentrations are representative of the lower atmosphere in most of the world.

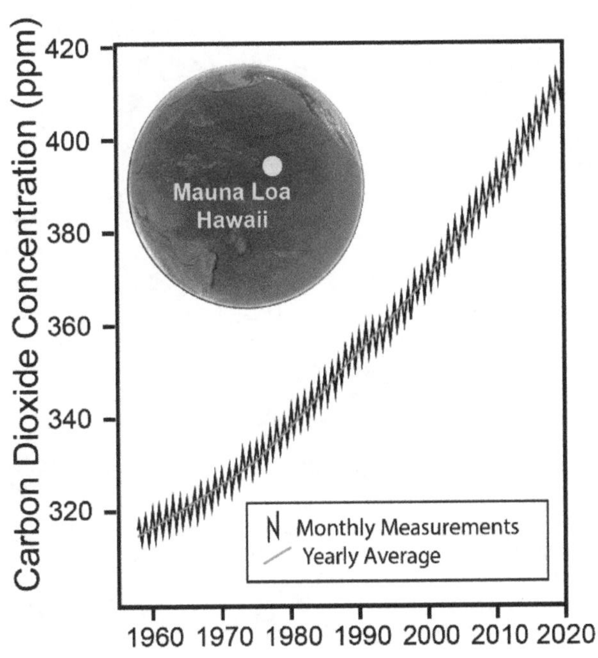

1. Approximately what was the average concentration of CO_2 in 1960? ________
2. Approximately what was the average concentration of CO_2 in 2020? ________
3. By about what percent did CO_2 concentrations increase between 1960 and 2020?

   ____

4. Prior to the industrial revolution in the 1800s, the average concentration of CO_2 was about 280 ppmv. By approximately what percent have CO_2 concentrations increased from their pre-industrial value? ____________
5. If CO_2 concentrations continue to increase at the 1960-2020 rate, what will the concentration be in 2100? How does your answer compare to the pre-industrial value of 280 ppmv? ________________________________
6. By about how many ppmv do CO_2 concentrations decrease from May to September (and increase from October to May? ____________
7. Provide a reason why CO_2 concentrations decrease from May to September.

Name: ______________________ Class: __________ Date: __________

Exercise 5.4 – Global Climate Change: Myth or Fact?

Indicate whether each of the following statements is a True (T) or False (F).

1. _______ Carbon dioxide concentrations are now higher than at any time in the past 400,000 years

2. _______ The Northern Hemisphere's average temperature was higher during the past decade than at any time in the past 1000 years

3. _______ Carbon dioxide is the strongest contributor to the atmosphere's natural greenhouse effect.

4. _______ The decade of 2021-2030 is certain to be warmer than the decade of 2011-2020.

5. _______ The interior regions of the continents are projected to experience the greatest greenhouse-driven warming during the present century.

6. _______ Trends of precipitation during the 20th century are inconsistent with greenhouse scenarios of climate change.

7. _______ The recent increase of carbon dioxide concentration could be due to natural factors because similar rates of increase have been documented in the paleoclimatic record.

8. _______ Climate models project increased precipitation and wetter soils in the western United States and Europe.

9. _______ Carbon dioxide concentrations are higher in late summer than in late winter because plants are net producers of carbon dioxide.

10. _______ Humans have had effects on carbon dioxide concentrations through land use as well as through the burning of fossil fuels.

11. _______ Warming during the next century is expected to change sea level by a greater amount than the changes that have occurred during glacial cycles of the past million years.

12. _______ Carbon dioxide concentrations varied through a greater range during the glacial-interglacial transitions than they have during the past 200 years.

13. _______ Two of the greatest uncertainties in projections of future climate change are the roles of clouds and the oceans.

Name: ______________________________ Class: ____________Date: __________

Exercise 6.1 – Environmental Lapse Rates

The sounding below shows the temperature measured over a single location. Compute the environmental lapse rate for each layer of the atmosphere listed below. Use the standard atmosphere altitudes on the bar on the left to determine altitudes. Identify inversion layers (they will have a negative lapse rate.) Note the minus sign. This is used because a positive lapse rate implies that temperature is decreasing with altitude.

$$\text{Lapse Rate} = -\frac{\text{change in temperature (°C)}}{\text{change in height (km)}} = \frac{-(T_{top} - T_{bottom})}{(H_{top} - H_{bottom})}$$

surface to 1 km – (10°C - 0°C) / (1 km – 0 km) = *– 10 °C/km*

1 to 3 km ______________

3 to 5 km ______________

5 to 7 km ______________

7 to 8 km ______________

8 to 10 km ______________

10 to 12 km ______________

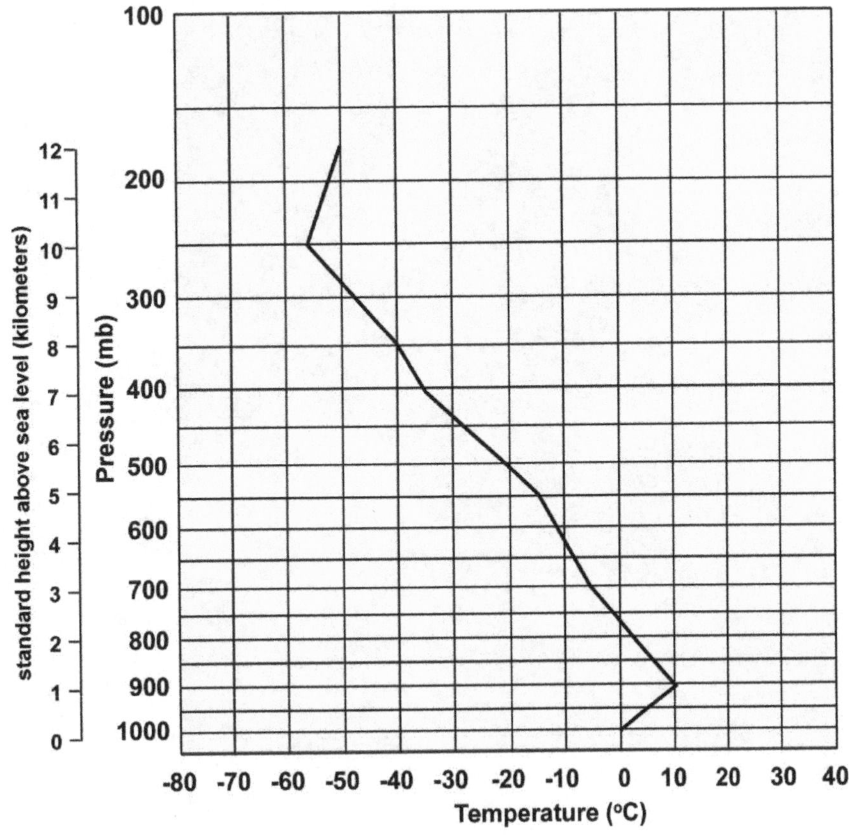

Name: ______________________________ Class: ___________Date: _________

Exercise 6.2 – Lifting Mechanisms

Thunderstorms are reported for each of the states listed below. Circle all possible lifting mechanism(s) for each state.

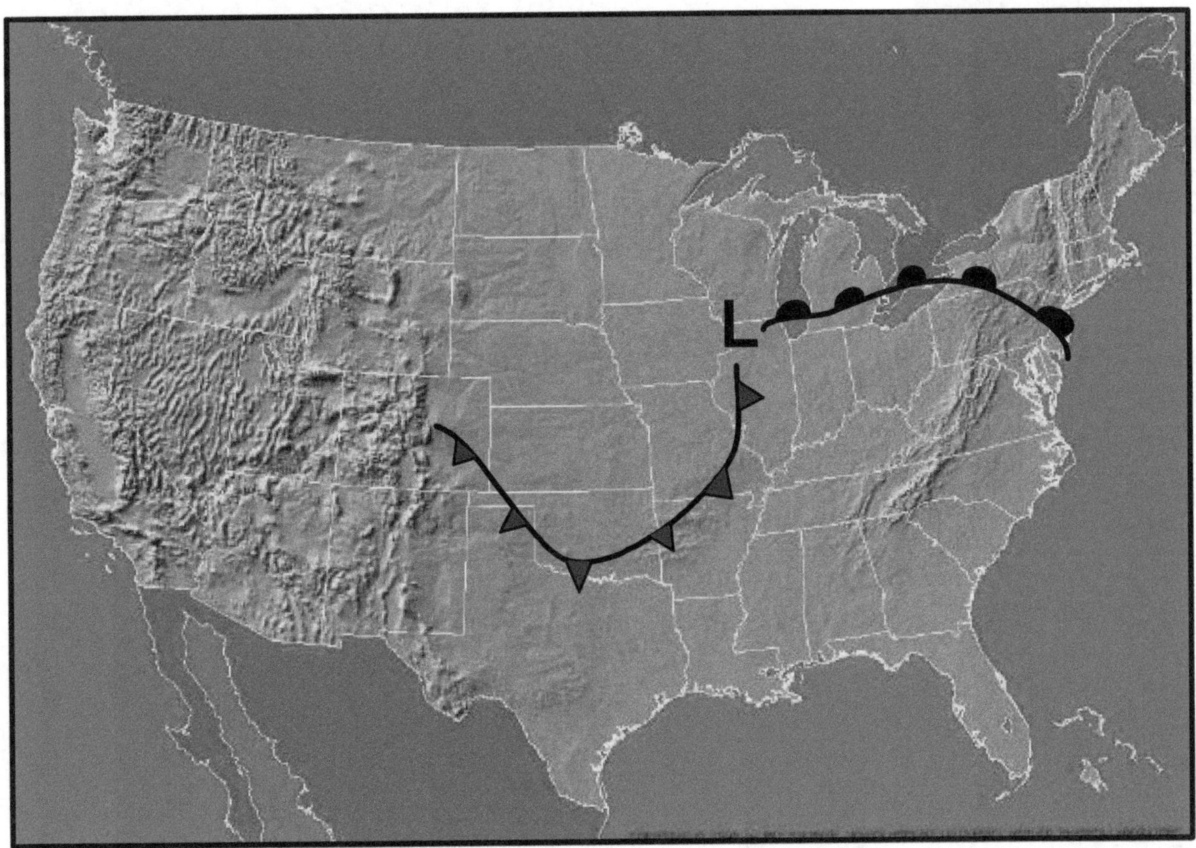

1. California	frontal lifting	sea breeze	topography
2. Illinois	frontal lifting	sea breeze	topography
3. Florida	frontal lifting	sea breeze	topography
4. Michigan	frontal lifting	sea breeze	topography
5. New York	frontal lifting	sea breeze	topography

Name: ______________________________ Class: __________ Date: __________

Exercise 6.3 – Stability and Soundings

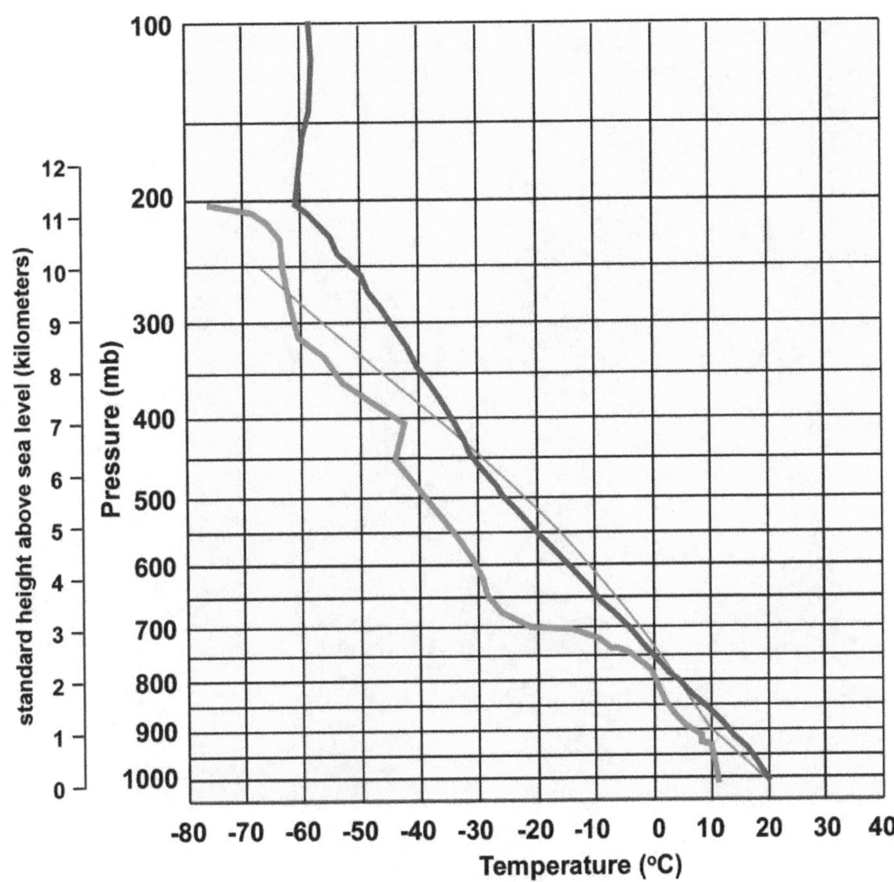

The sounding above depicts temperature and dewpoint temperature as thick black lines. The temperature of a lifted parcel is also shown as the thin red line. Answer 1 through 6 using this data.

1. Which thick line is the temperature, the one on the right or left? __________
2. Which thick line is the dewpoint temperature (right or left)? __________
3. At approximately what pressure is the level of free convection? __________
4. If a parcel is lifted to the level of free convection, to what pressure level will buoyancy enable it to rise? __________
5. At what pressure level is the lifting condensation level? __________
6. At what pressure level is the cloud base? __________
7. Estimate the value of the Lifted Index. __________

Name: ______________________ Date: ______________________

Name: ______________________________ Class: ____________Date: __________

Exercise 6.4 – Lifted Index and Thunderstorm Development

Thunderstorms require three environmental conditions for development. These three conditions must all be present at the same time in the same location:

1. sufficient moisture
2. a lifting mechanism
3. instability

The map below shows the value of the Lifted Index (contoured) and the locations of fronts on a day in late spring. Assume that there is sufficient moisture available across the entire U.S.

(a) Based on the information on the map, determine where thunderstorms are most likely to form and place the *thunderstorm symbol* in that location or locations.

(b) Briefly explain why you selected that particular location.

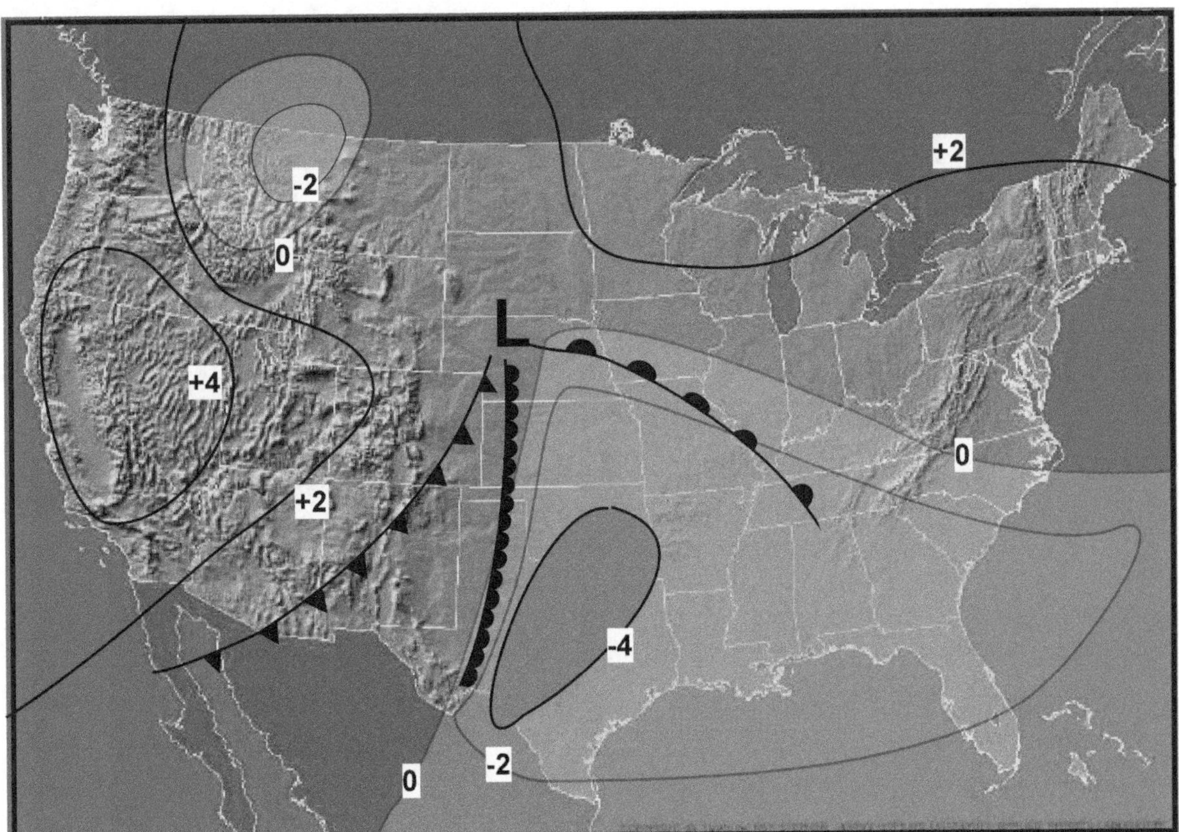

Name: ______________________________ Class: __________ Date: _________

Exercise 7.1 – Forces in the Atmosphere

PGF = Pressure Gradient Force
CF = Coriolis Force
FR = Frictional Force
GR = Gravitational Force

Place letters on the blanks in each statement to make the statement correct.

1. The __________ acts to reduce the speed of air.
2. The __________ acts to accelerate air horizontally from rest.
3. The __________ is zero at the equator and increases with latitude.
4. The __________ is always directed toward lower values of pressure.
5. The __________ can change the direction air moves, but not its speed.
6. The strength of the __________ is visualized on a surface map by isobars.
7. The __________ is an apparent force associated with the rotation of the Earth.
8. The __________ is strongest near the earth's surface and decreases in importance at higher altitudes.
9. In the Northern Hemisphere, the __________ always acts opposite the direction of air motion, but the __________ always acts to the right of the air motion.
10. For weather applications, the magnitude of the __________ acting on any air parcel can be considered constant throughout the troposphere.
11. Except for very close to the surface, __________ acts primarily through the mixing of parcels of air moving at different speeds.

Name: ______________________________ Class: ___________Date: _________

Exercise 7.2 – The Horizontal Pressure Gradient Force

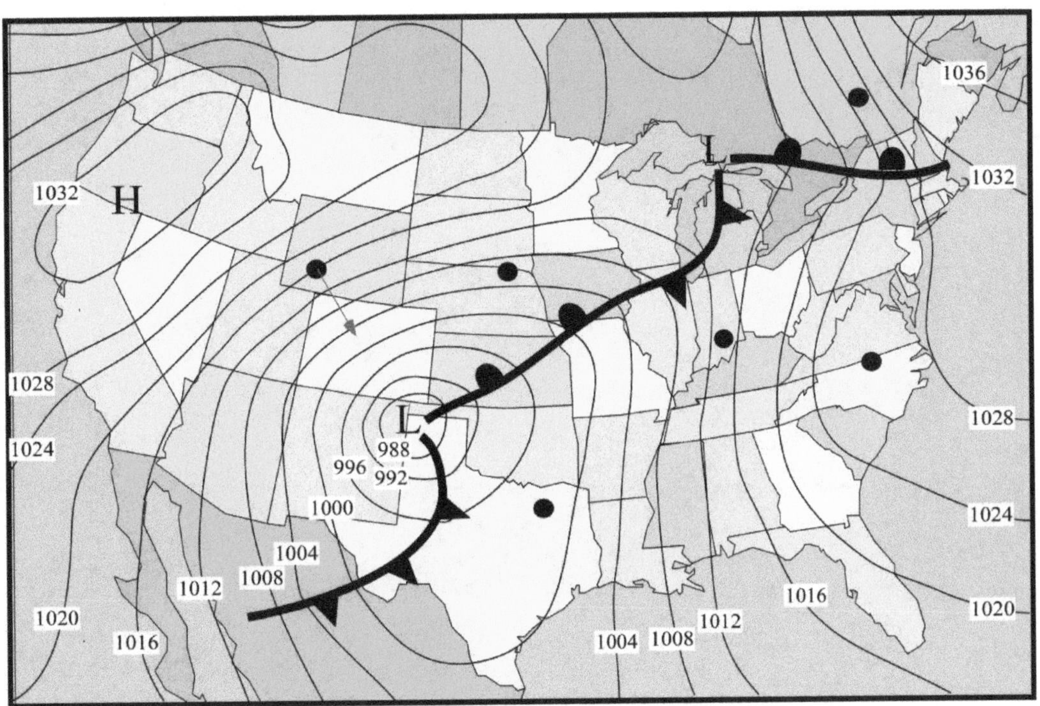

1. At each of the six large black dots on the map above, draw an arrow emerging from the dot to indicate the direction of the pressure gradient force (PGF). Adjust the length of your arrows so that a long arrow indicates a relatively strong PGF and a short arrow indicates a relatively weak PGF. Wyoming has been done for you.

2. What is the pressure at the dot in Wyoming?

3. What is the average value of the pressure gradient between the black dot in Wyoming and the low-pressure center (986 mb) centered southeast of Colorado? Assume the distance between these two points is approximately 500 km.

4. Denver, in central Colorado, is approximately 20 kilometers in diameter, and about halfway between the dot in Wyoming and low pressure center. What is the approximate pressure change (in mb) across Denver?

Name: ______________________________ Class: ___________Date: __________

Exercise 7.3 – The Geostrophic Wind

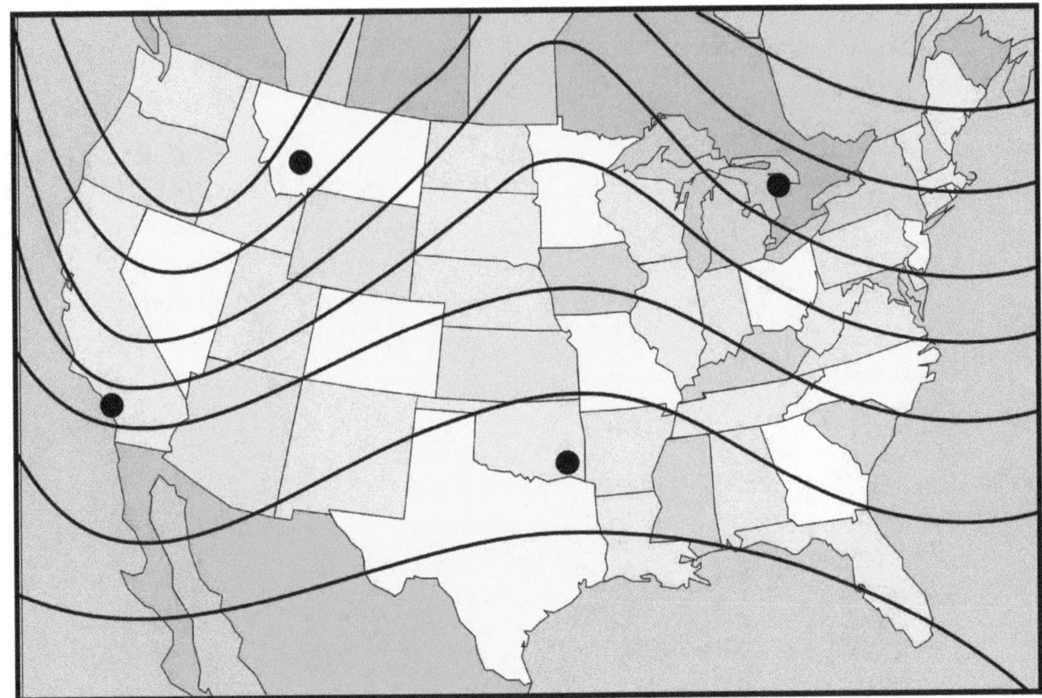

Assume that the flow represented on the 500 mb map above is in geostrophic balance.

1. Draw an arrow showing the speed and direction of the geostrophic wind at each of the four points indicated on the map. The "tail" of each arrow should start at the black dot and the length of the arrow should be proportional to wind speed.

2. Draw a second arrow at each point that represents the pressure gradient force (PGF). Again, the tail of the arrow should start at each black dot, the arrow should point in the direction the force acts, and the length of the arrow should represent the relative strength of the PGF. Label the arrow "PGF".

3. Do the same as in (2), but for the Coriolis Force. Label the arrow "CF".

Name: ______________________________ Class: ___________Date: __________

Exercise 7.4 – Fronts and the Jet Stream

1. The maps on the left are surface maps depicting positions of frontal boundaries and low- and high-pressure centers. The maps on the right depict wind speed at 300 mb, with the light shading indicating winds exceeding 70 knots and the dark shading indicating winds exceeding 100 knots. Match the surface map with the jet stream.

   Map A matches Map _________

   Map B matches Map _________

   Map C matches Map _________

2. How did you determine the matching?

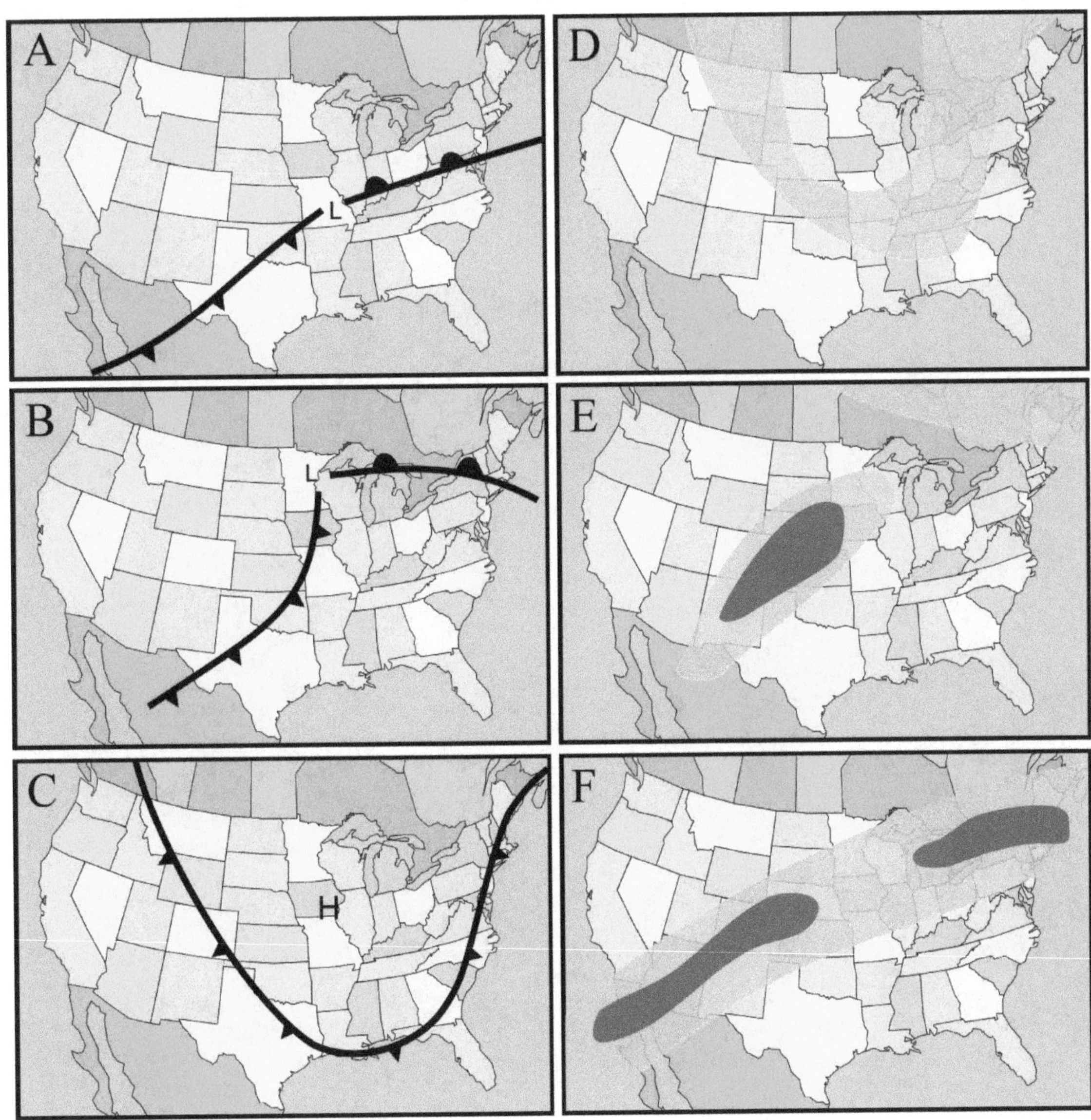

Name: ______________________________ Class: ___________Date: __________

Exercise 8.1 – Curvature Effect

For each map below:

1. Draw a line that bisects the trough. Label it "trough axis".
2. Circle the divergent region of the trough and place a "D" in the circle.
3. Draw a square around the convergence region of the trough and place a "C" in it.
4. Where would you expect a surface pressure to drop most rapidly? Why?

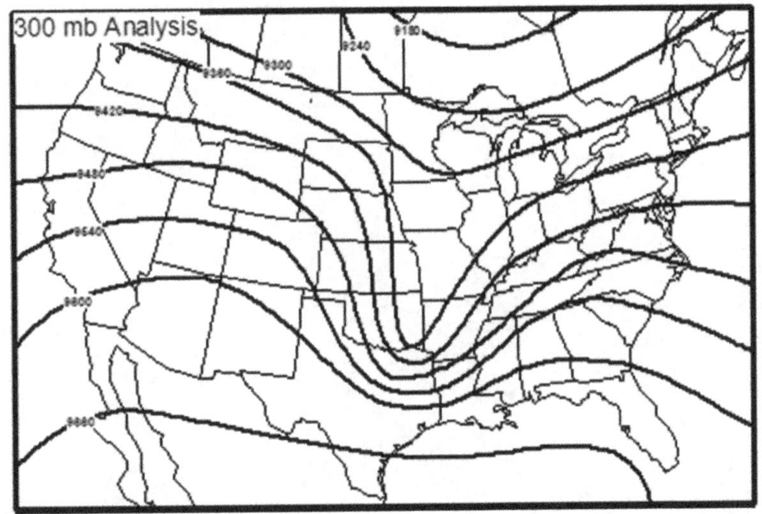

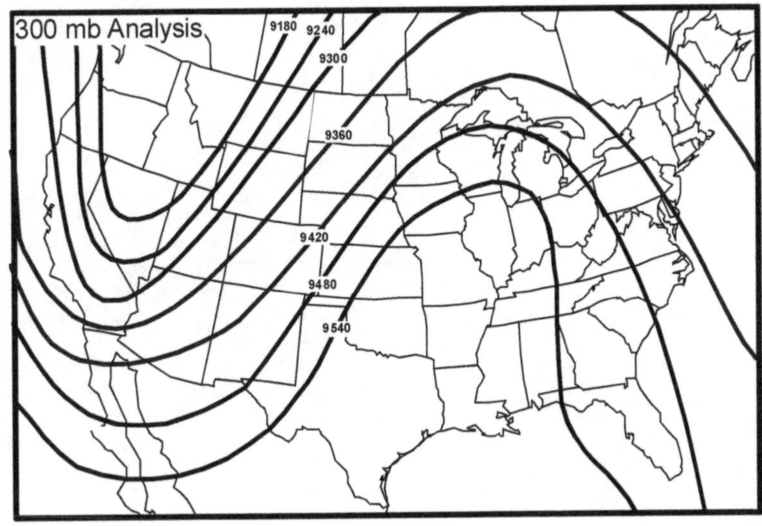

Name ____________ Class ____________ Date ____________

Exercise 8.[illegible] [illegible]

Refer to [illegible] below:

1. Draw a line that marks the trough. Label it Trough a[illegible]

2. Circle the divergent region of the trough and place a [illegible]

3. Draw a square around the convergence region of the trough and place [illegible]

4. Where would you [illegible] surface pressure to [illegible]

Name: ______________________________ Class: ___________Date: _________

Exercise 8.2 – Jet Streak Effect

Shaded areas on the maps below indicate wind speeds over 100 knots (light shading) and 140 knots (dark shading). For each map below:

1. Draw two lines, one along the axis of the jet stream and the other dividing the jet streak into its entrance and exit regions.
2. Label the divergent region(s) of the jet streaks with a "D".
3. Label the convergent region(s) of the jet streaks with a "C".
4. Consider where convergence and divergence occur with the curvature effect. Place an "L" at locations you would expect surface pressure to drop most rapidly.

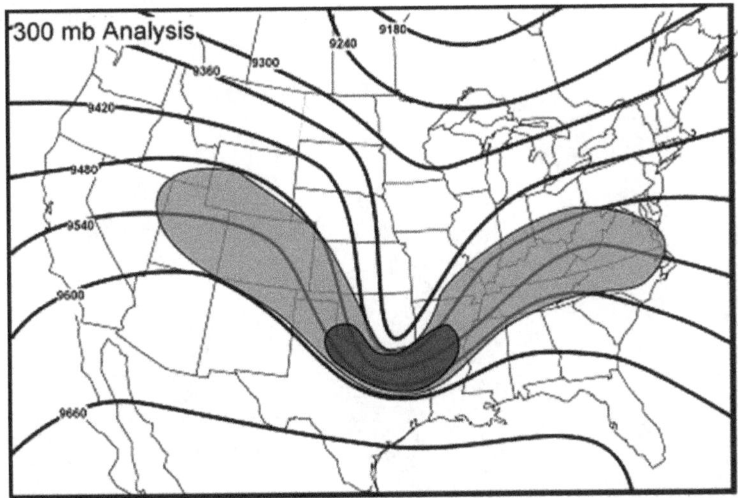

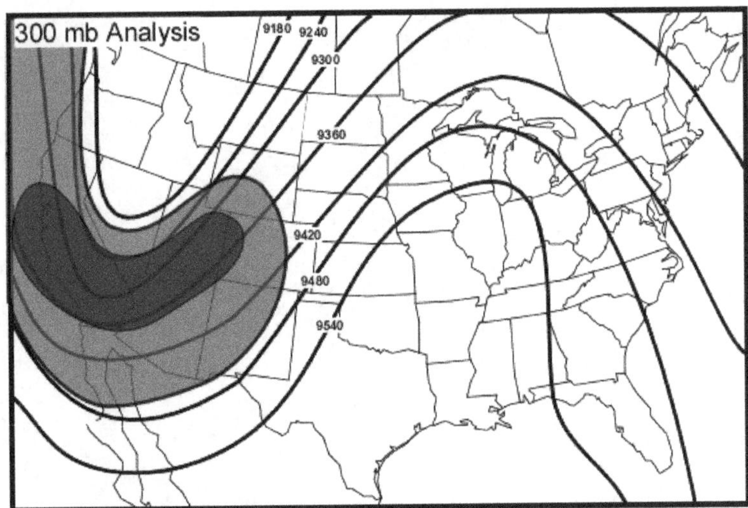

Name: ______________________________ Class: ___________Date: _________

Exercise 8.3 – Convergence and Divergence & Surface Systems

The diagrams below indicate convergence or divergence near Earth's surface (lower arrows) and in the upper troposphere (higher arrows) above surface pressure centers (Highs or Lows). In each case, the length of the arrows indicates the strength of the convergence or divergence. For each diagram:

1. Write "H" or "L" between the arrows at the surface to show whether the surface pressure center is a High or a Low.
2. Draw an arrow above each surface pressure center to indicate the direction of vertical air motion (upward or downward).
3. Circle "S" or "W" to indicate whether the surface system will Strengthen or Weaken.
4. If a surface low-pressure center strengthens how does its pressure change? ________
5. If a surface low-pressure center weakens how does its pressure change? ________
6. If a surface high-pressure center strengthens how does its pressure change? ________
7. If a surface high-pressure center weakens how does its pressure change? ________

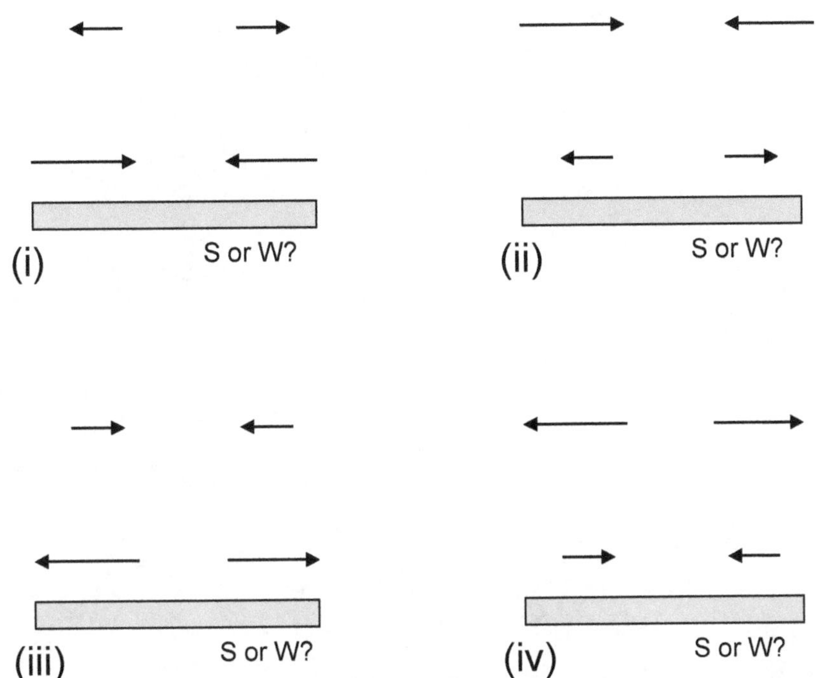

Name: ______________________________ Class: ___________Date: _________

Exercise 8.4 – Friction and its Effect on Winds

Circle the correct answer from the choices in parentheses.

1. Friction (increases, decreases) the wind speed.

2. Friction results in a reduction of the (pressure gradient force, Coriolis force).

3. The top of the friction layer is generally near (850 mb, 300 mb).

4. Friction ultimately causes the wind to deflect (into, out of) a surface high-pressure system.

5. Friction causes (convergence, divergence) of surface winds around a low-pressure center.

6. Friction contributes to (upward, downward) motion above a surface high-pressure center.

7. The friction layer will generally be deeper at (mid-afternoon, sunrise).

8. In airflow that would otherwise be in geostrophic balance, friction causes a (rightward, leftward) deflection.

9. Friction causes air to spiral (inward, outward) around a surface low-pressure center.

10. In the Southern Hemisphere, the Coriolis force acts 90 degrees to the left of the wind. In this case, friction will act (in the same direction as, opposite to) the wind.

11. Over water, friction deflects the wind from its geostrophic direction by an angle that is typically (10° to 20°, 20° to 40°).

12. The angle by which friction deflects the wind from its geostrophic value generally becomes (larger, smaller) with increasing altitude in the atmosphere.

13. If the only convergence and divergence in the atmosphere resulted from friction, surface highs would (strengthen, weaken) over time, while surface lows would (strengthen, weaken) over time.

Name: ______________________________ Class: ___________Date: _________

Exercise 8.5 – High and Low Pressure Centers

Characteristics of high- and low-pressure centers in the Northern Hemisphere are listed below. In each case, indicate by **H** or **L** whether the statement applies to high- or low-pressure centers. If a statement is valid for both types of centers, place both **H** and **L** in the blank space.

1. _____ Surface winds are divergent.
2. _____ Winds blow counter-clockwise.
3. _____ Favored by cooling of an air column.
4. _____ Lower pressure is to the left of the winds.
5. _____ Winds spiral inward toward the pressure center.
6. _____ Generally located to the east of an upper-air trough.
7. _____ Surface winds are deflected to the left of the isobars.
8. _____ Associated with convergence in the upper troposphere.
9. _____ Pressure gradient force points away from the pressure center.
10. _____ Associated with subsidence, dry air, and generally clear skies.
11. _____ Vertical motions are downward above the surface pressure center.
12. _____ Wind speeds (in the absence of friction) are slower than geostrophic.
13. _____ Release of latent heat favors intensification of the surface pressure center.
14. _____ Clouds and precipitation generally occur above the surface pressure center.

Name: ______________________________ Class: __________ Date: _________

Exercise 9.1 – Airmass Identification

1. Write in the two-letter abbreviation for each of the airmass descriptors below.
   (continental, c; maritime, m; Polar, P; Tropical, T)

   (a) dry and warm ________

   (b) moist and warm ________

   (c) moist and cold ________

   (d) dry and cold ________

2. For each of the following reports of temperature and dewpoint, identify the type of airmass that is affecting the city. Use the two letter abbreviations identified above.

	City	Month	Temp.	Dewpt.	Airmass
(a)	Washington, DC	January	39	37	________
(b)	Boston, MA	July	81	71	________
(c)	Milwaukee, WI	January	24	8	________
(d)	Chicago, IL	August	79	69	________
(e)	Oklahoma City, OK	August	93	48	________
(f)	Dallas, TX	March	70	63	________
(g)	Bismark, ND	June	82	41	________
(h)	Kansas City, MO	December	38	6	________
(i)	Salt Lake City, UT	July	92	30	________
(j)	Seattle, WA	October	48	45	________

Name: ______________________________ Class: ___________Date: _________

Exercise 9.2 – Which Front Passed the Station?

Each pair of station models below shows data from the same station six hours apart. During that time, a front passed the station. Based on the station models, determine what type of front passed by choosing from the list. Use each selection only once. Draw in the front symbol as it would appear on a weather map.

C	Cold Front		D	Dry Line
W	Warm Front		U	Upper Level Front
O	Occluded Front			

BEFORE	AFTER	FRONT	MAP SYMBOL
31 142 29	54 136 42	____	
85 087 74	83 122 37	____	
73 032 65	56 052 38	____	
78 142 68	80 136 67	____	
33 998 29	24 020 21	____	

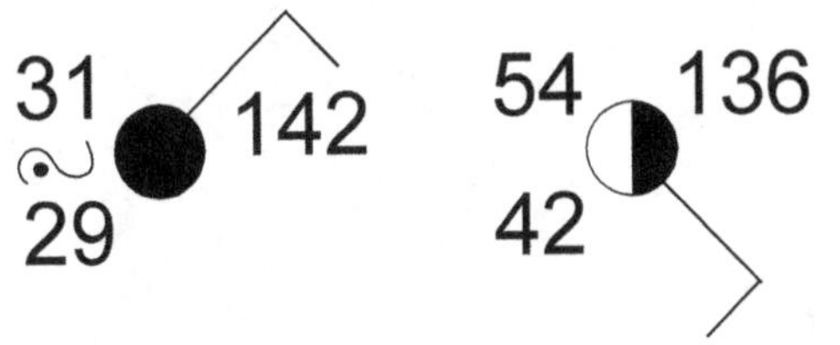

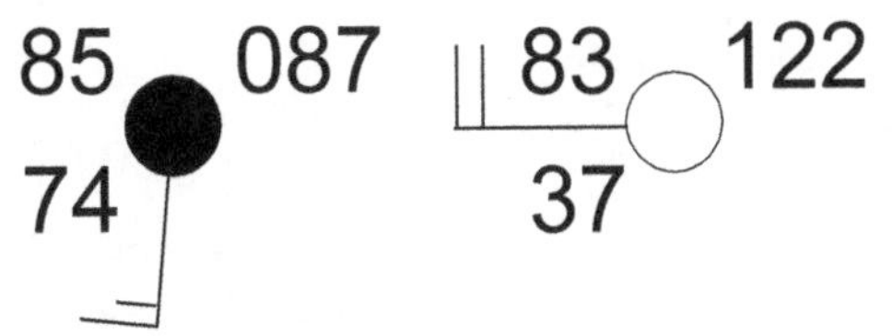

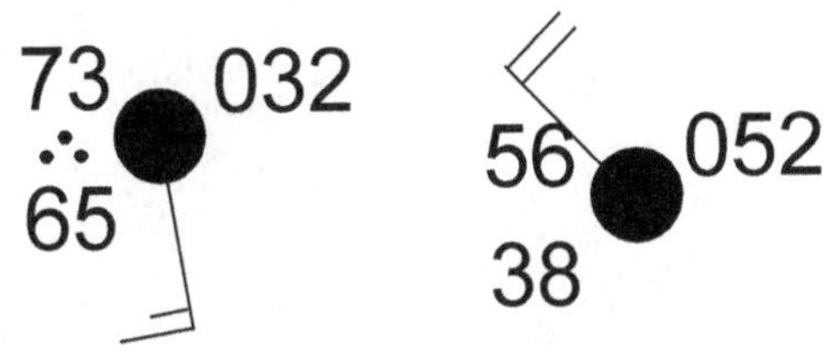

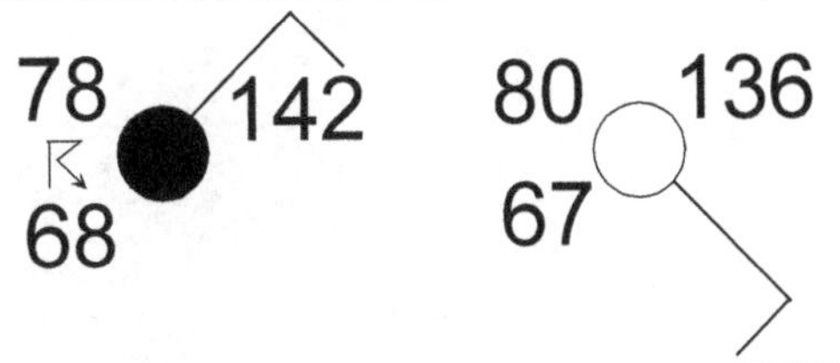

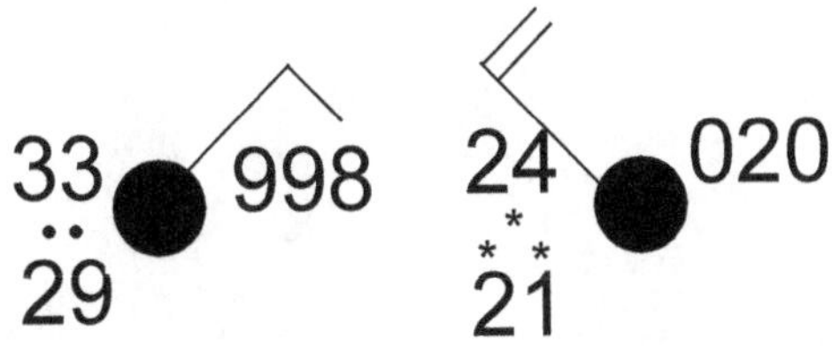

Name: ______________________________ Class: ____________Date: __________

Exercise 9.3 – Can You Find the Cold Front?

Carefully examine the surface station data on the map below.

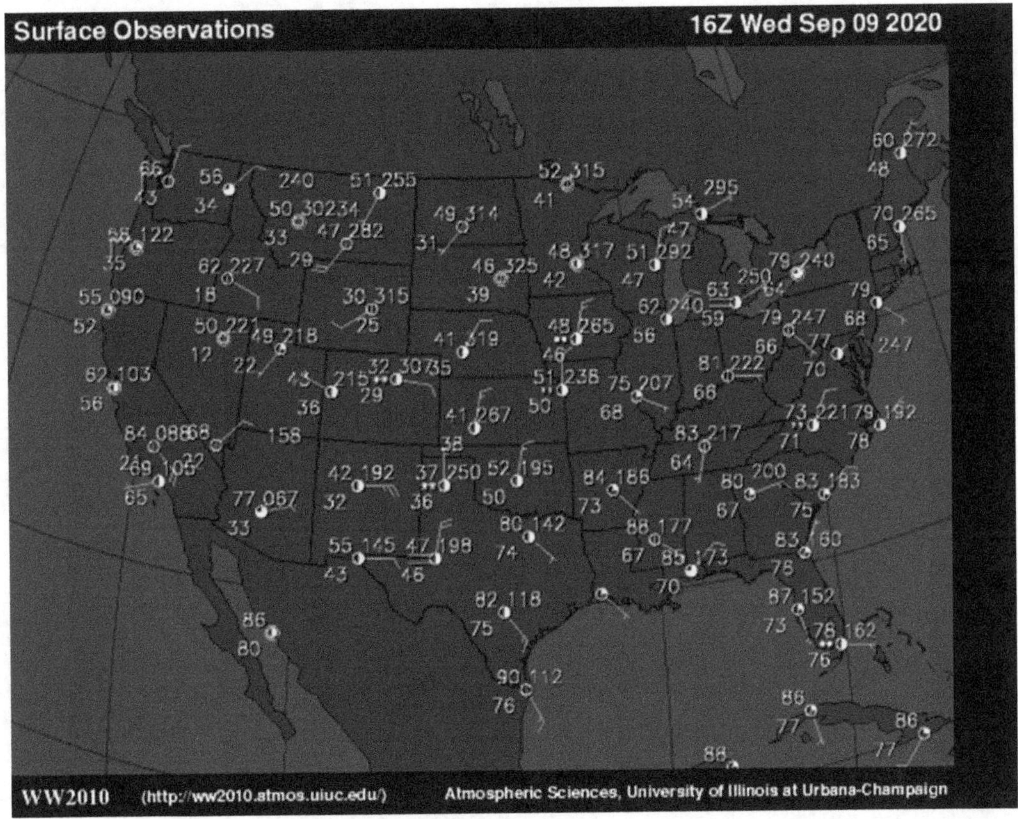

1. Draw in the location of cold front with the correct frontal symbols.

2. How did you determine the location of the front? (e.g. what data did you use?)

____

3. What direction is the front moving? How do you know?

____

Name: ______________________________ Class: ____________Date: __________

Exercise 10.1 – Weather Conditions within a Cyclone

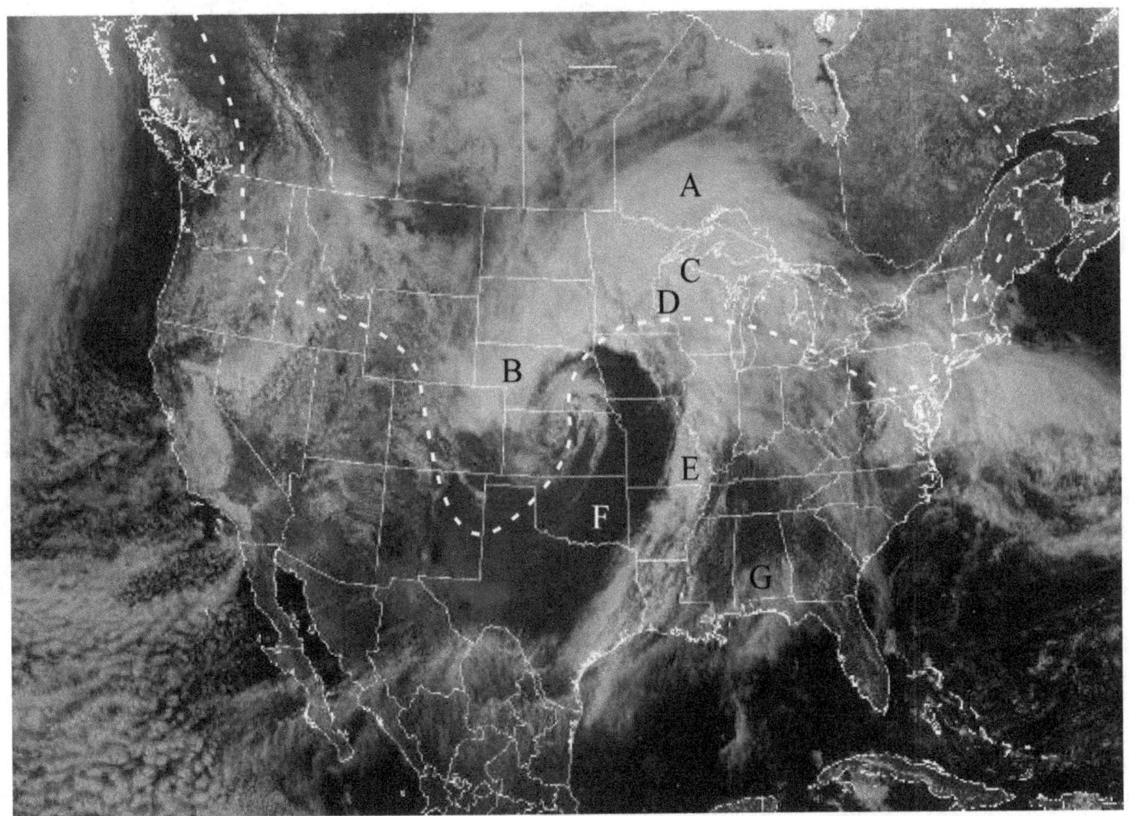

A visible satellite image of a Colorado cyclone over the central United States is shown above. The dashed line is the 0°C isotherm at the surface. Assume that the Colorado cyclone occurred during the first week of March with typical climatological conditions.

1. Place an L at the location of the low-pressure center.

2. Draw a line along the leading front to the southeast of the surface low-pressure center.

3. Draw station models that show wind direction, cloud cover, temperature (estimate based on how far the location is from the 0°C isotherm and position in the cyclone) and weather (use standard weather symbols) near the seven points labeled A through G on the image.

4. Of the seven locations, which would most likely be reporting snow? __________

5. Of the seven locations, which would most likely be reporting rain?__________

6. Of the seven locations, which would most likely be reporting sleet or freezing rain?

   ____

Name: ______________________________ Class: ___________Date: __________

Exercise 10.2 – Jet Streaks, Troughs and Surface Low-Pressure Centers

Below are four 300 mb maps covering a 36-hour period during which a strong cyclone developed and moved across the Great Plains.

1. On each map, place an "L" at the most likely position of the surface low-pressure center based on the position and orientation of the jet stream.

2. Sketch a cold front and a warm front in a reasonable position on each diagram.

3. Describe the direction the surface low tracks. Briefly explain why it follows this path.

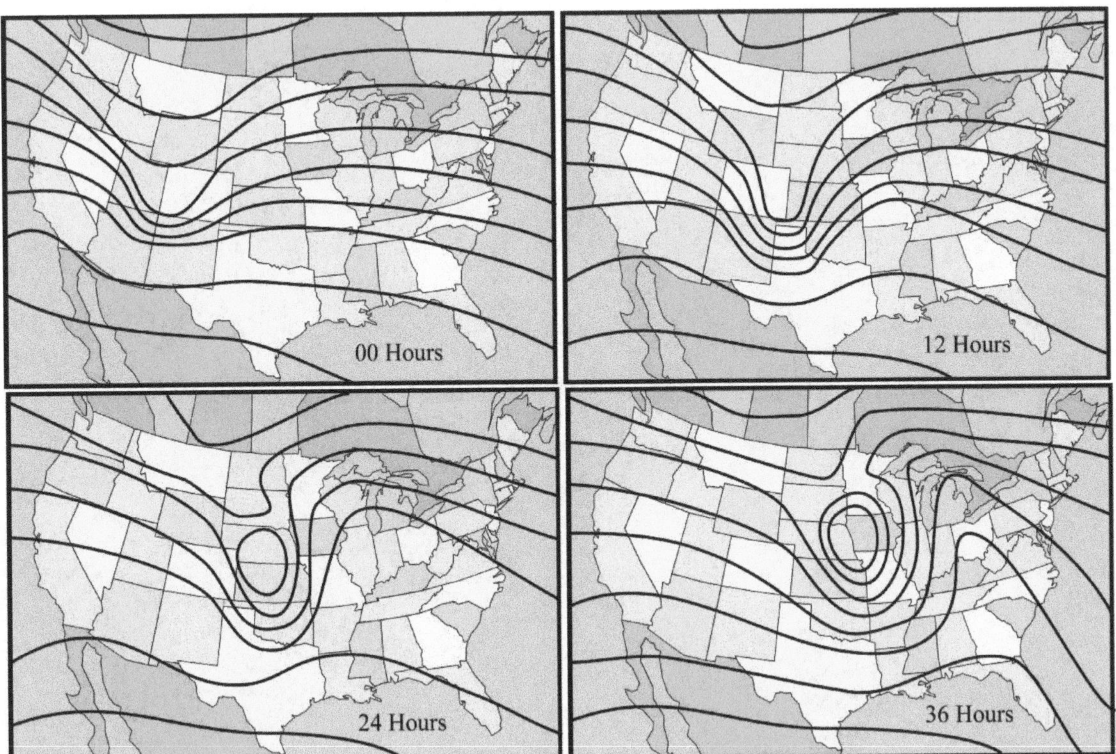

Name: ________________________________ Class: ____________Date: __________

Exercise 10.3 – Soundings through Cyclones

The map to the right shows a typical cyclone on the Great Plains.

The soundings at the bottom of the page were taken at each of the six points labeled A through F on the map. Write a letter in the blank in the upper right corner of each of the soundings to indicate which sounding corresponds to each point A through F.

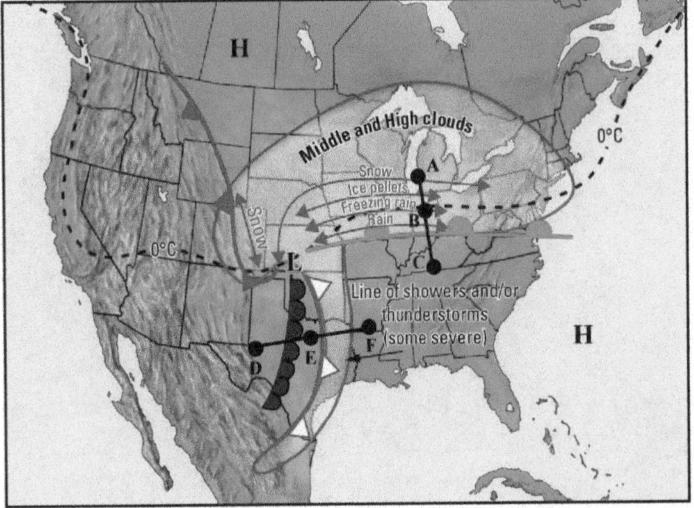

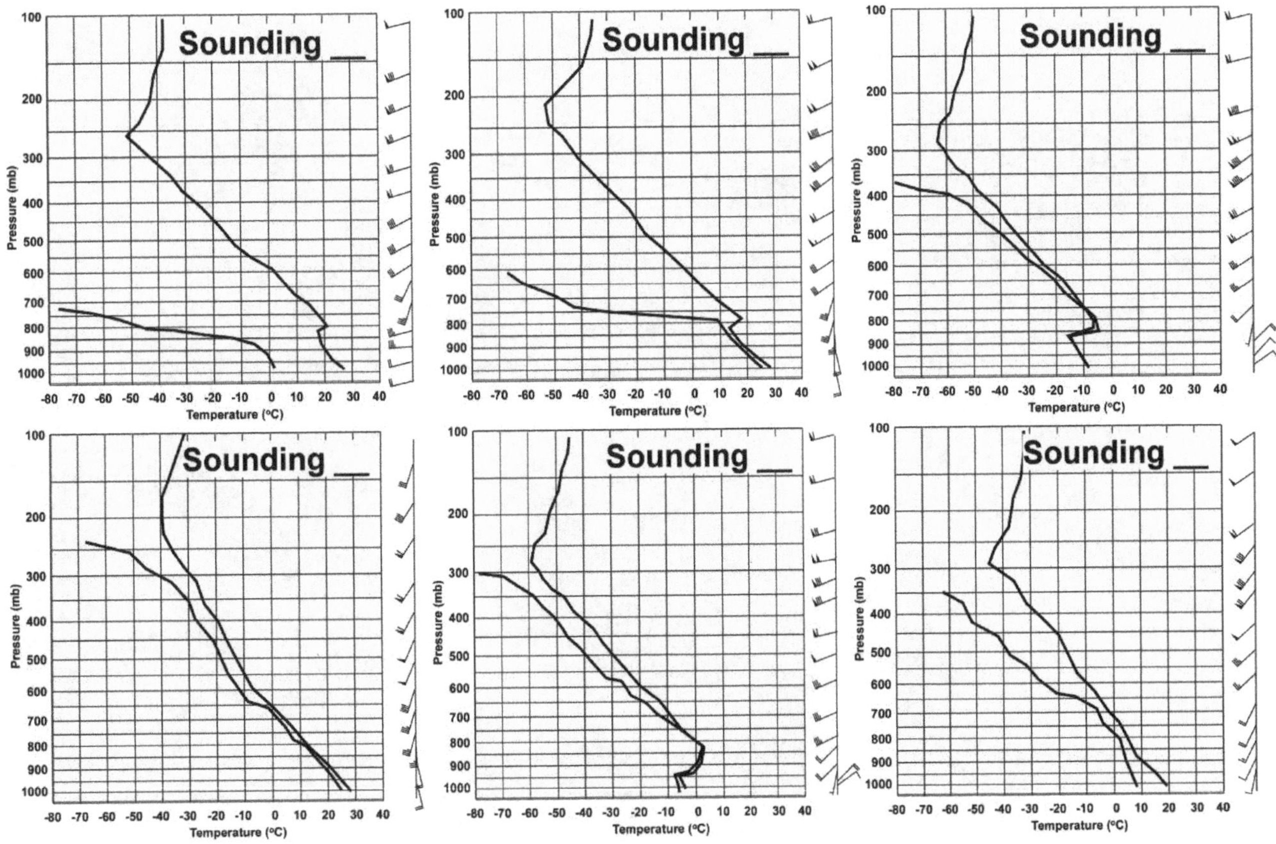

Name: ______________________________ Class: ___________Date: __________

Exercise 10.4 – Fronts in a Cyclone's Southern Sector

The left panels of the figure below show three surface cyclones over the Great Plains, each with different frontal structure south of the low-pressure center. The right panels are cross sections along the direction of the arrow in the corresponding figure to the left. The topography and a thunderstorm are shown on each cross section.

On the cross section diagram, sketch the front(s) as they would appear in the vertical.

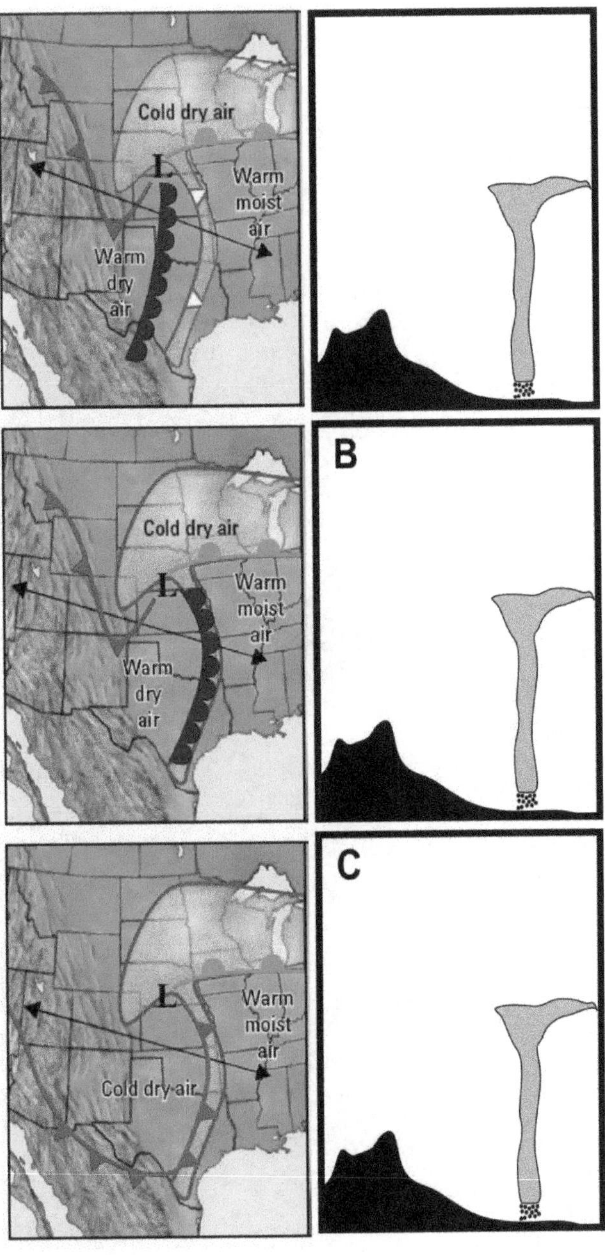

Name: ______________________________ Class: ___________Date: _________

Exercise 11.1 – The Rain-Snow Line and Nor'easters

The map at the bottom of the page shows the New York City area with the city itself shaded dark, and the metro-area shaded light. The boxes are 10 kilometers on a side. Assume that three Nor'easters pass up the coast during the winter season. The table provides, for each Nor'easter, 1) temperature of air over the ocean, 2) rate that air cooled for each land square it moves over, and, 3) wind speed. In all three cases, the wind was directly from the east. Treat a square as land if land occupies more than 50 percent of the square. If air moves over water again, don't count the water square.

(a) Fill in the missing data in the table.

	Air temp. over ocean (°F)	Degrees cooling to reach 32°F	Cooling rate of air (°F/hr)	Time to cool to 32°F	Wind speed (km/hr)	# squares air moves to cool to 32°F
Nor'easter #1	44		2		20	
Nor'easter #2	38		3		20	
Nor'easter #3	33		3		20	

(b) Draw in the rain-snow line at the time the observations above were taken for each of the three Nor'easters listed above. Label the lines #1, #2, and #3.

(c) If a forecaster issued a forecast for heavy snow in New York, would the forecast be a boom (accurate) or a bust (missed forecast) for each case? Assume that if less than about 70% of the city or metro gets snow, it's a bust. How about if the forecast was issued for the Metro area rather than the city itself? (Fill in the blanks to the right of the map.)

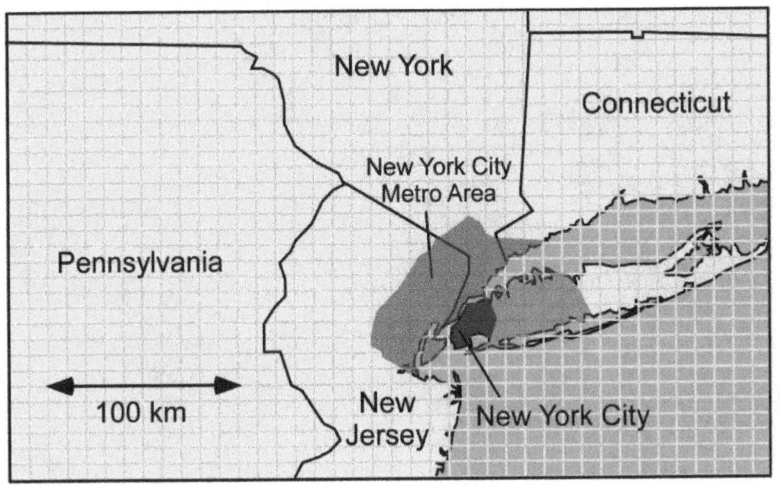

Boom or Bust?

	CITY	METRO
1.	_______	_______
2.	_______	_______
3.	_______	_______

Name: ______________________________ Class: ___________Date: __________

Exercise 11.2 – Interacting Jet Streak Circulations

Often with East Coast cyclones, multiple jet streaks work together to create a strong surface cyclone. The two upper air maps below show the height field (solid lines) and jet streak locations where the wind speed exceeds 100 knots (shaded). Map A shows conditions 24-hours prior to Map B.

1. On both maps, place a "D" in the quadrants of each jet streak where divergence is occurring.

2. On Map B, place one "L" where an intense low-pressure system is most likely to develop at the surface. Explain briefly below why you chose that location.

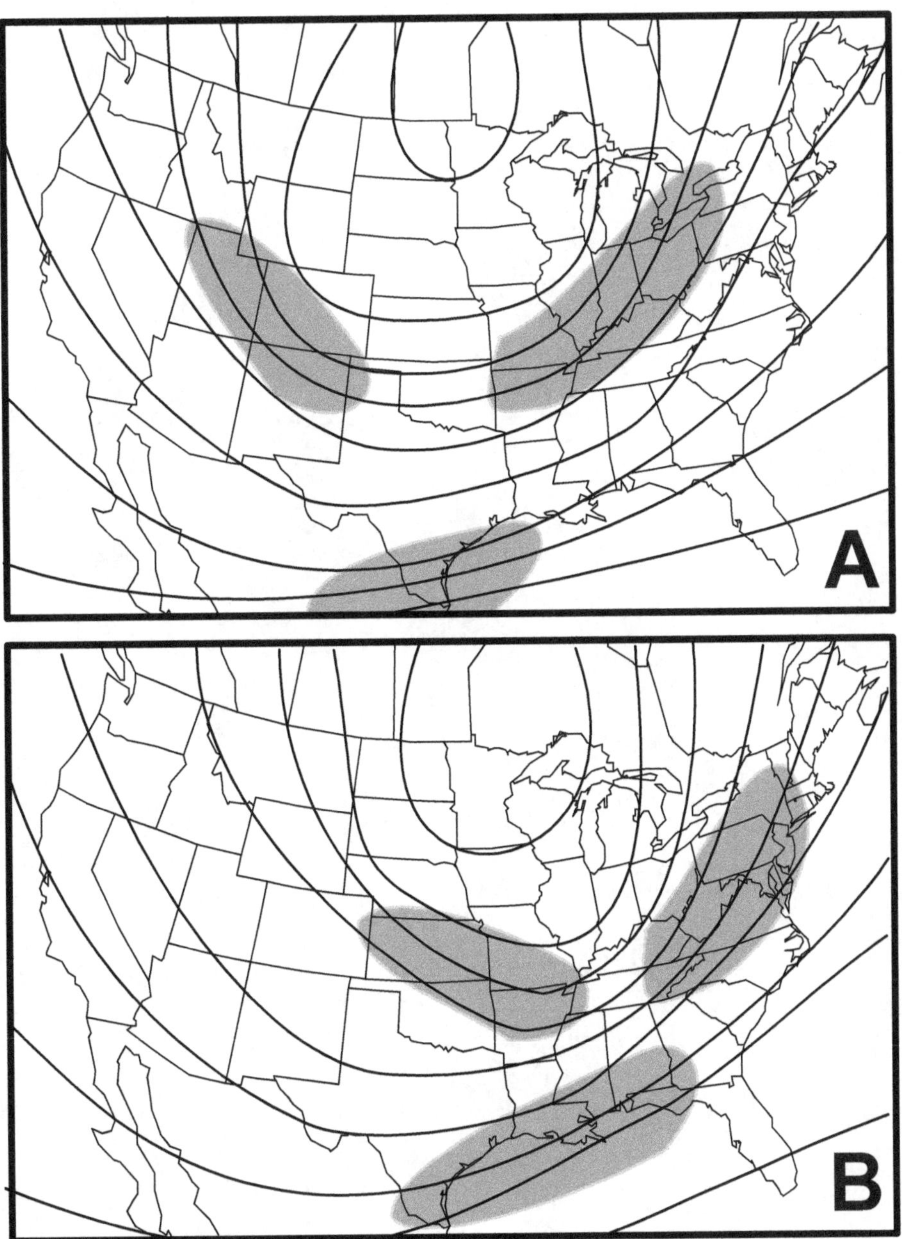

Name: ______________________________ Class: ___________Date: __________

Exercise 11.3 – Where is the Low-Pressure Center During Heavy Snow?

1. On each map below, place an "L" at the location where a strong surface low-pressure center would be located to produce a heavy snowfall in the highlighted city.

2. On each diagram, sketch in the entire region that would likely experience the largest snow totals, relative to the center of the low. Assume the low tracks from southwest to northeast.

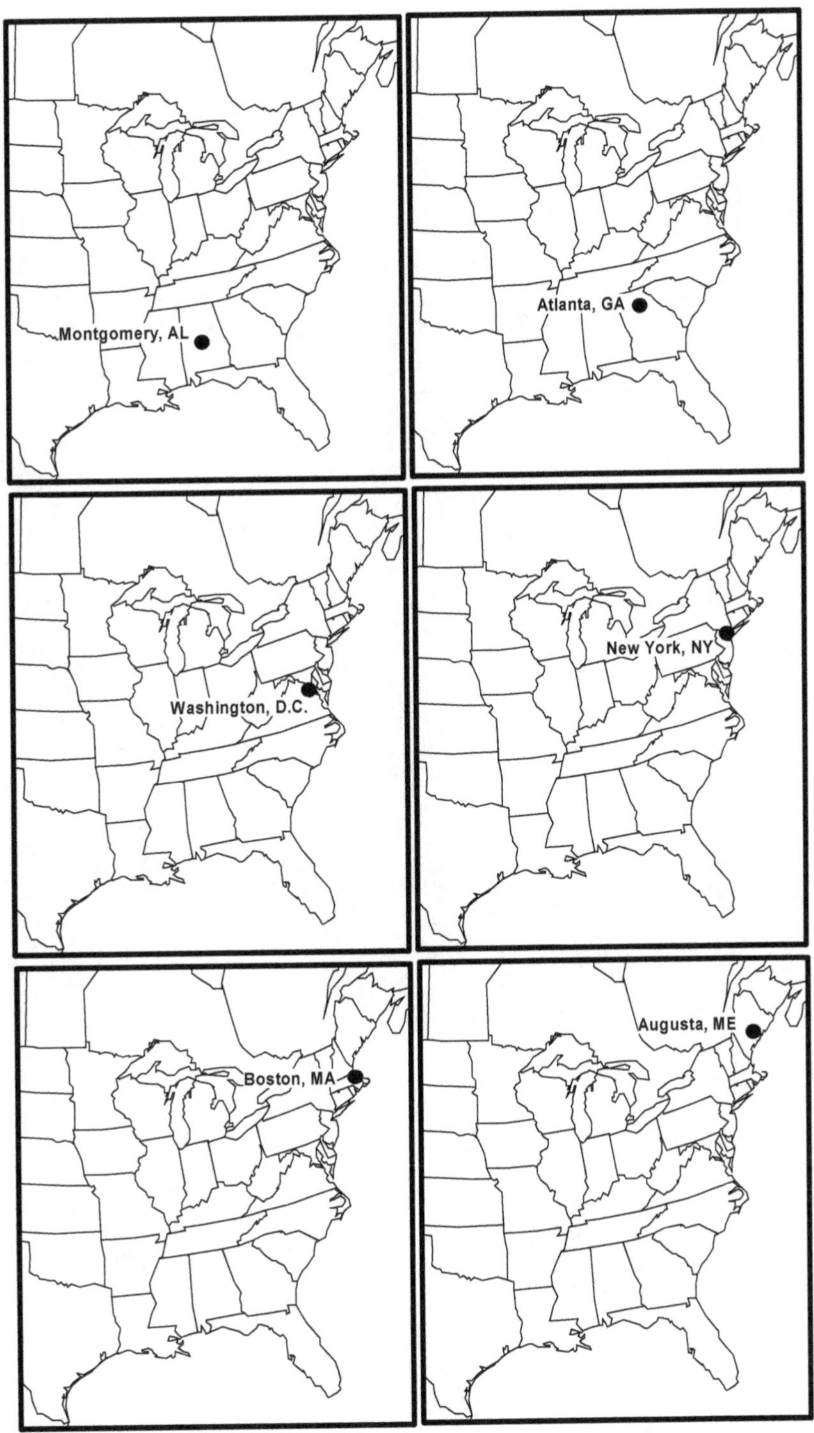

Name: ______________________________ Class: ____________ Date: __________

Exercise 11.4 – Wind Direction and Nor'easters

The map on the bottom of the page shows the track of a strong cyclone at 12-hour intervals. The storm brought snowfall and hazardous winter weather conditions to the eastern United States. Using your knowledge of airflow around a cyclone, determine the wind direction (N, NE, E, SE, S, SW, W, NW) at locations A, B and C at the times listed.

Location	14 Feb 0000 UTC	14 Feb 1200 UTC	15 Feb 0000 UTC	15 Feb 1200 UTC
A				—
B				
C	—			

At what time would you classify this cyclone as a nor'easter? Why?

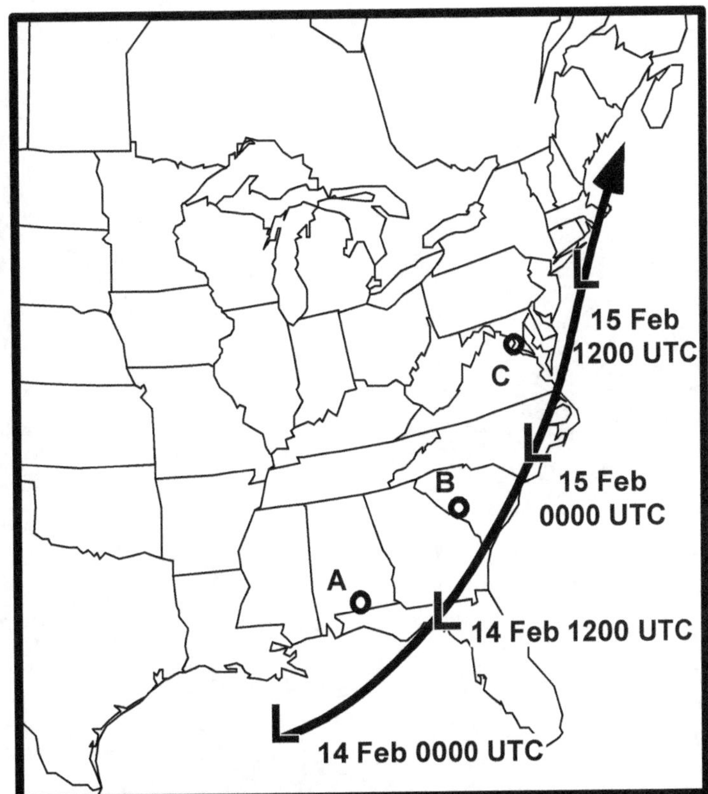

Name: ______________________________ Class: __________Date: __________

Exercise 12.1 – Where Will Freezing Precipitation Occur?

The maps below show analyses of sea level pressure and fronts for four weather systems over the central United States. Shaded areas denote cloud cover. The 0°C isotherm for the surface is also indicated on each map. Assume for this exercise that precipitation is falling everywhere that clouds are present. On each of the maps, outline the regions that are likely to be experiencing freezing rain or freezing drizzle. If no freezing rain is likely, write that on the map.

Briefly explain why you chose the areas you did. ✩ typically north of 0°C line

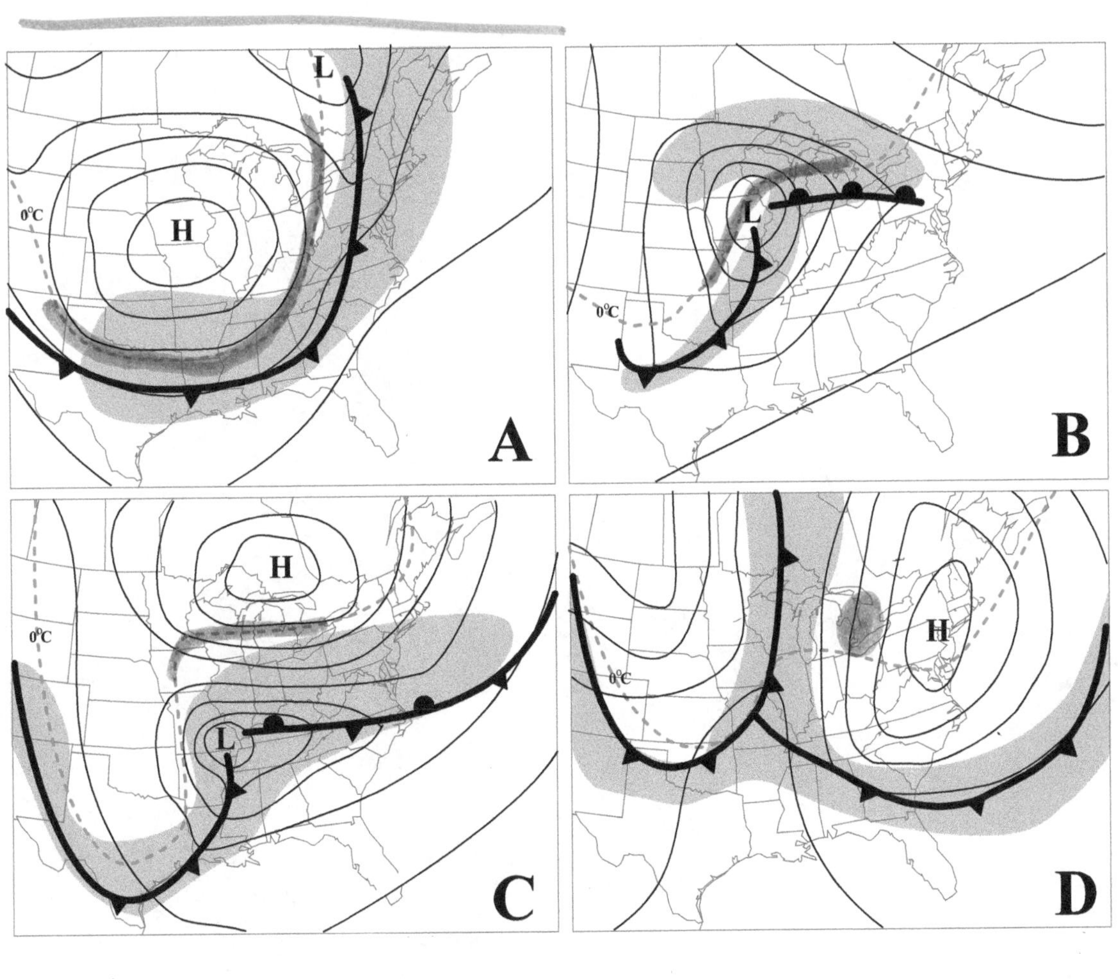

Name: ______________________ Class: __________ Date: __________

Exercise 12.2 – Fronts, Soundings and Precipitation Type

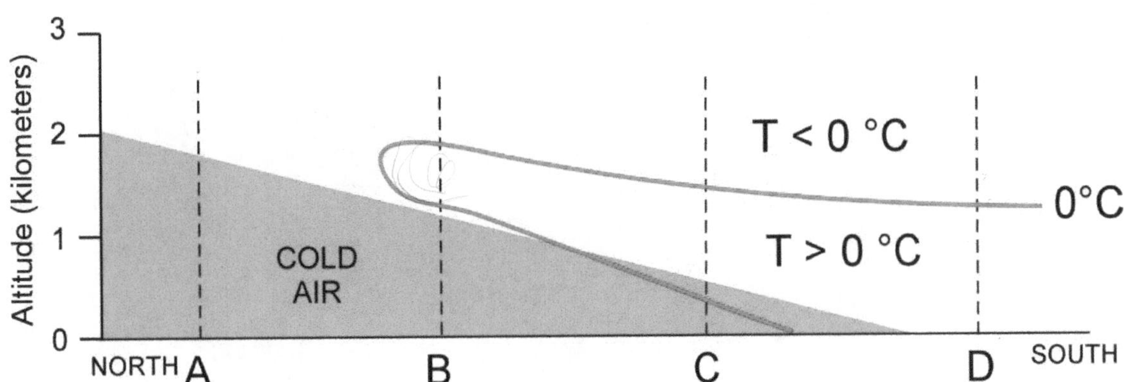

1. On the cross section above, freezing rain formed via the melting process is most likely to occur at point __________.

2. Based on the cross section, snow is most likely to occur at point __________.

3. Based on the cross section, rain is most likely to occur at point __________.

4. Based on the cross section, sleet is most likely to occur at point __________.

Soundings were launched at points corresponding to locations A, B, C, and D. The temperature profiles from the soundings, in no particular order, are shown on diagrams E, F, G, and H. Match the temperature profiles to cross section.

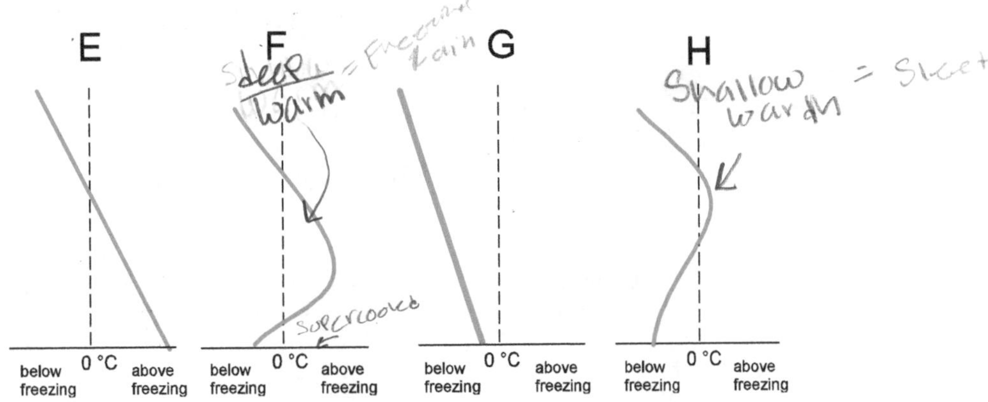

5. Which sounding would have been launched in freezing rain that formed via the melting process? __________

6. Which sounding would have been launched in rain? __________

7. Which sounding would have been launched in snow? __________

8. Which sounding would have been launched in sleet? __________

Name: ______________________________ Class: __________ Date: _________

Exercise 12.3 – Distribution of Freezing Precipitation and Global Change

1. Freezing precipitation (rain and drizzle) is predominant in certain areas of North America. Shade in the regions on the maps below that are most likely to experience freezing rain and freezing drizzle in today's climate.

2. Based on your knowledge of freezing precipitation and trends in global climate change, to the right of the image provide a brief forecast for how patterns of freezing precipitation may change in the next few decades.

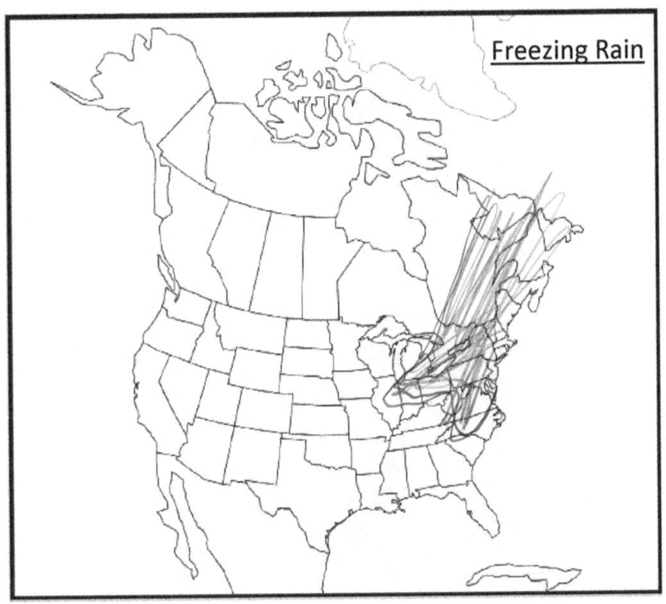

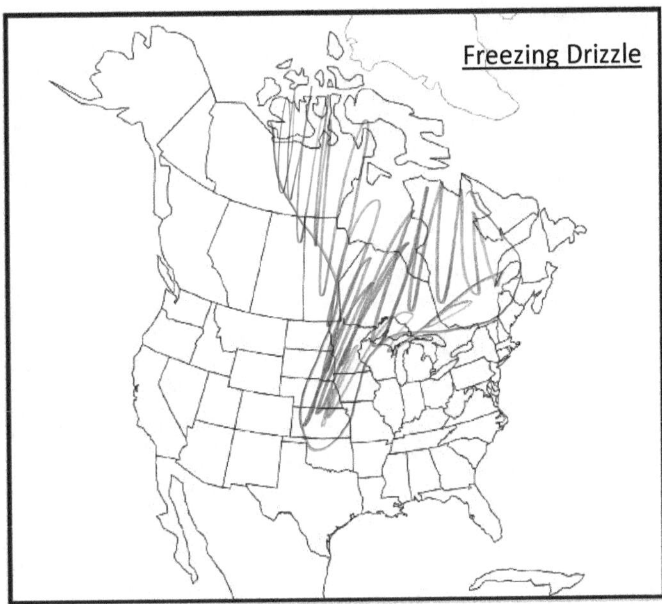

Name: ______________________________ Class: ____________Date: __________

Exercise 12.4 – Freezing Drizzle Versus Freezing Rain

Each statement describes a type of freezing precipitation (or both). Identify the type of precipitation by circling the appropriate abbreviation: ZR (freezing rain), ZL (freezing drizzle), or B (both freezing rain and freezing drizzle).

1. ZR ZL B Leads to the development of an ice glaze
2. ZR ZL B Can occur in the atmosphere when the temperature of the air aloft is below freezing from the ground to the tropopause
3. ZR ZL B Typically is responsible for significant ice storms that produce millions of dollars in damage
4. ZR ZL B Can lead to traffic accidents.
5. ZR ZL B Is the primary cause of aircraft icing
6. ZR ZL B Has the highest frequency of occurrence in the northeastern United States and Canada
7. ZR ZL B Has the highest frequency of occurrence in south-central Canada
8. ZR ZL B Occurs when snow aloft falls into a warm layer where the air is above freezing, melts, and then supercools is a subfreezing layer of air near the surface
9. ZR ZL B Is composed of supercooled water
10. ZR ZL B Does not require a temperature inversion aloft
11. ZR ZL B Can freeze upon contact with cars, trees and road surfaces
12. ZR ZL B Accumulation may lead to power outages, disrupt air and ground transportation and cause considerable property damage.

Name: ______________________ Class: __________ Date: __________

Exercise 13.1 – Lake-Effect Processes

The diagram below shows a cross section across Lake Michigan. It is wintertime. Air temperature to the west of the lake is -25°C (-13°F) and the water temperature is 1°C (34°F). The wind is from the west and a lake effect snowstorm is in progress.

1. Each statement below applies to a location indicated by one of the black dots on the diagram. Place the appropriate letter in a blank next to one of the dots.

   A. Convergence occurs at this location.

   B. Divergence occurs at this location.

   C. Air is descending and skies are generally clear at this location.

   D. Air is ascending and heavy snow is falling at this location.

   E. Heat and moisture are transferred from the lake to the air at this location.

2. Draw clouds on this diagram as they might appear during a lake effect storm.

3. Draw arrows to indicate the direction of horizontal air motion during a lake effect storm.

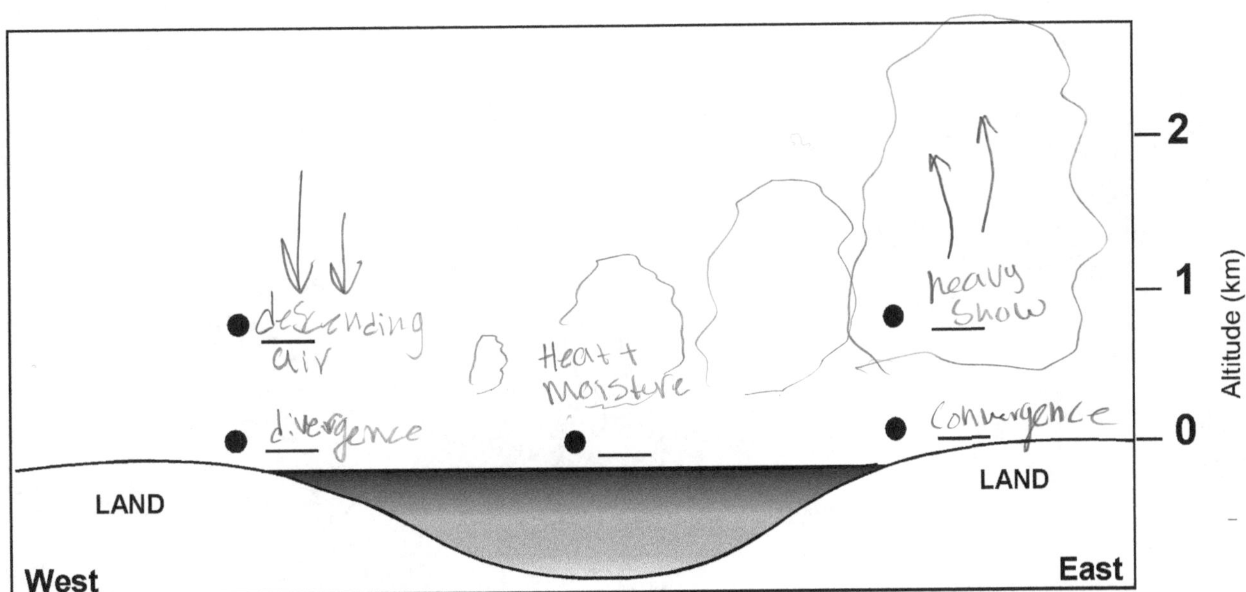

Name: ______________________________ Class: ___________ Date: _________

Exercise 13.2 – Lake Effect Snow Organizations

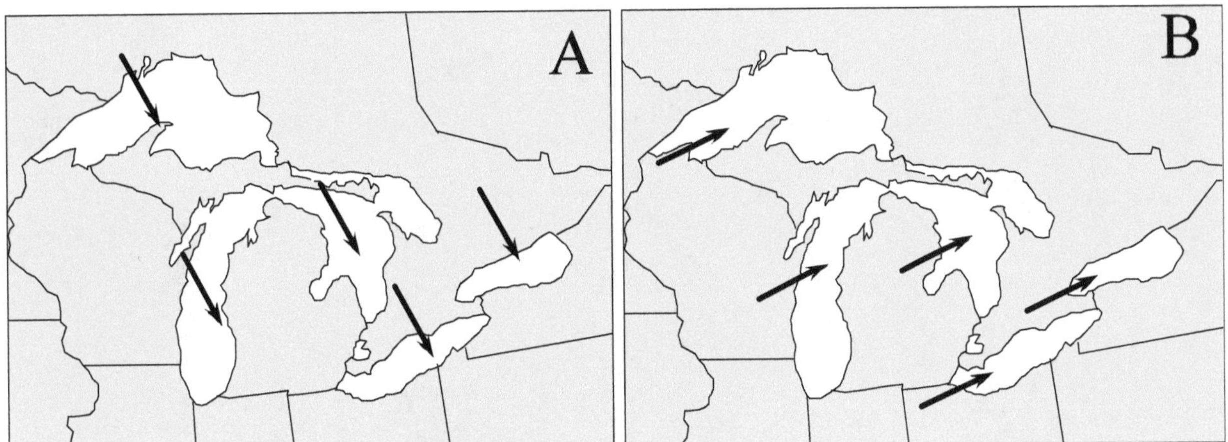

1. Label each of the Great lakes (H) Huron, (O) Ontario, (M) Michigan, (E) Erie, and (S) Superior.

For questions 2 and 3, circle the appropriate words to make the statements true.

2. Wind-parallel rolls form when winds are (fast, slow) and blow parallel to the (long, short) axis of the lake.

3. Shore-parallel bands form when winds are weak or when winds blow parallel to the (long, short) axis of the lake.

4. Assume that very cold air (< -25°C; -13°F) is moving over warm water (1°C; 34°F) at a (fast) rate of 25 mph. Would you expect wind-parallel rolls (WPR) or shore-parallel bands (SPB) to form on each lake? Fill in the blanks with either WPR or SPB. If both are plausible, answer BOTH.

PANEL A		PANEL B	
Lake Superior	________	Lake Superior	________
Lake Michigan	________	Lake Michigan	________
Lake Huron	________	Lake Huron	________
Lake Erie	________	Lake Erie	________
Lake Ontario	________	Lake Ontario	________

Name: ______________________________ Class: ___________Date: __________

Exercise 13.3 – Wind Direction & Lake Effect Snow

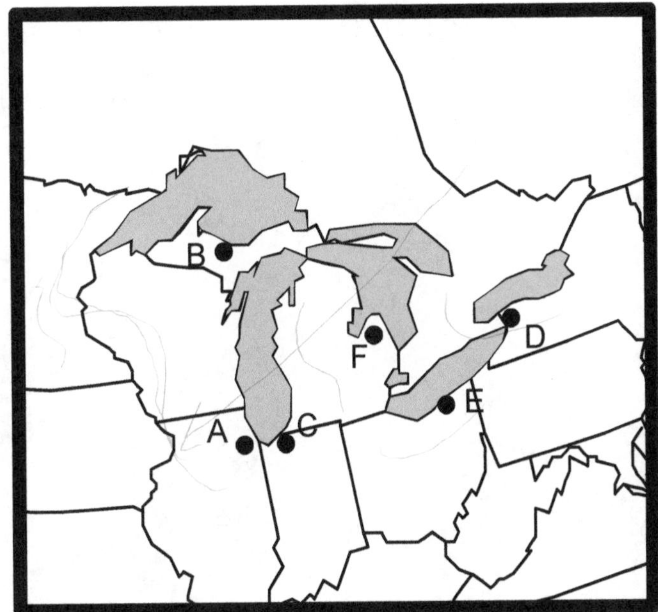

1. What direction would the wind need to be in order to get lake effect snow in:

   A. Chicago, IL ______________

   B. Marquette, MI ______________

   C. Gary, IN ______________

   D. Buffalo, NY ______________

   E. Cleveland, OH ______________

   F. Flint, MI ______________

2. The prevailing wind direction across the Great Lakes is northwest. Shade in where you would expect to find lake effect snow. (Take in to consideration how far inland lake effect snow typically falls.)

3. Why do you think there is rarely lake effect snow on the northern shores of the lakes?

   wind doesnt come from there

Name: ______________________________ Class: ___________Date: __________

Exercise 14.1 – Wind Chill Temperatures

Temperature (°F)

Wind (mph)	40	35	30	25	20	15	10	5	0	-5	-10	-15	-20	-25	-30	-35	-40	-45
Calm	40	35	30	25	20	15	10	5	0	-5	-10	-15	-20	-25	-30	-35	-40	-45
5	36	31	25	19	13	7	1	-5	-11	-16	-22	-28	-34	-40	-46	-52	-57	-63
10	34	27	21	15	9	3	-4	-10	-16	-22	-28	-35	-41	-47	-53	-59	-66	-72
15	32	25	19	13	6	0	-7	-13	-19	-26	-32	-39	-45	-51	-58	-64	-71	-77
20	30	24	17	11	4	-2	-9	-15	-22	-29	-35	-42	-48	-55	-61	-68	-74	-81
25	29	23	16	9	3	-4	-11	-17	-24	-31	-37	-44	-51	-58	-64	-71	-78	-84
30	28	22	15	8	1	-5	-12	-19	-26	-33	-39	-46	-53	-60	-67	-73	-80	-87
35	28	21	14	7	0	-7	-14	-21	-27	-34	-41	-48	-55	-62	-69	-76	-82	-89
40	27	20	13	6	-1	-8	-15	-22	-29	-36	-43	-50	-57	-64	-71	-78	-84	-91
45	26	19	12	5	-2	-9	-16	-23	-30	-37	-44	-51	-58	-65	-72	-79	-86	-93
50	26	19	12	4	-3	-10	-17	-24	-31	-38	-45	-52	-60	-67	-74	-81	-88	-95
55	25	18	11	4	-3	-11	-18	-25	-32	-39	-46	-54	-61	-68	-75	-82	-89	-97
60	25	17	10	3	-4	-11	-19	-26	-33	-40	-48	-55	-62	-69	-76	-84	-91	-98

Frostbite Times: 30 minutes; 10 minutes; 5 minutes

$$\text{Wind Chill (°F)} = 35.74 + 0.6215T - 35.75(V^{0.16}) + 0.4275T(V^{0.16})$$

Where, T= Air Temperature (°F) V= Wind Speed (mph) *Effective 11/01/01*

The chart above is used by the National Weather Service to estimate wind chill temperature and how long it will take before exposed skin freezes. Fill in the table and determine which city has the coldest wind chill. (Estimate the wind chill temperature by interpolation when necessary.)

City	Temperature (°F)	Wind Speed (mph)	Wind Chill Temp. (°F)	Time to Frostbite (min)
Green Bay, WI	0	15		
Boise, ID	-5	15		
Columbus, OH	5	20		
Grand Rapids, MI	-15	10		
Lincoln, NE	-10	20		
Denver, CO	5	40		
St. Louis, MO	0	30		
Portland, ME	-15	20		
Des Moines, IA	-10	35		
Bismarck, ND	-15	45		

City with lowest wind chill temperature: ______________________________

Name: ______________________________ Class: ___________Date: _________

Exercise 14.2 – The Progression of a Cold Wave

The six weather maps show the surface (left) and upper air (right) conditions during a cold wave.

1. The surface maps are presented in random order. Label the maps in the space to the left "time 1", "time 2" and "time 3" to put the maps in chronological order.

2. Draw a line connecting the surface map with the upper air map that represents the conditions aloft at that time.

3. What would be a realistic time span for the time lapsed between each set of maps (e.g., several hours, a day, several days, several weeks)?

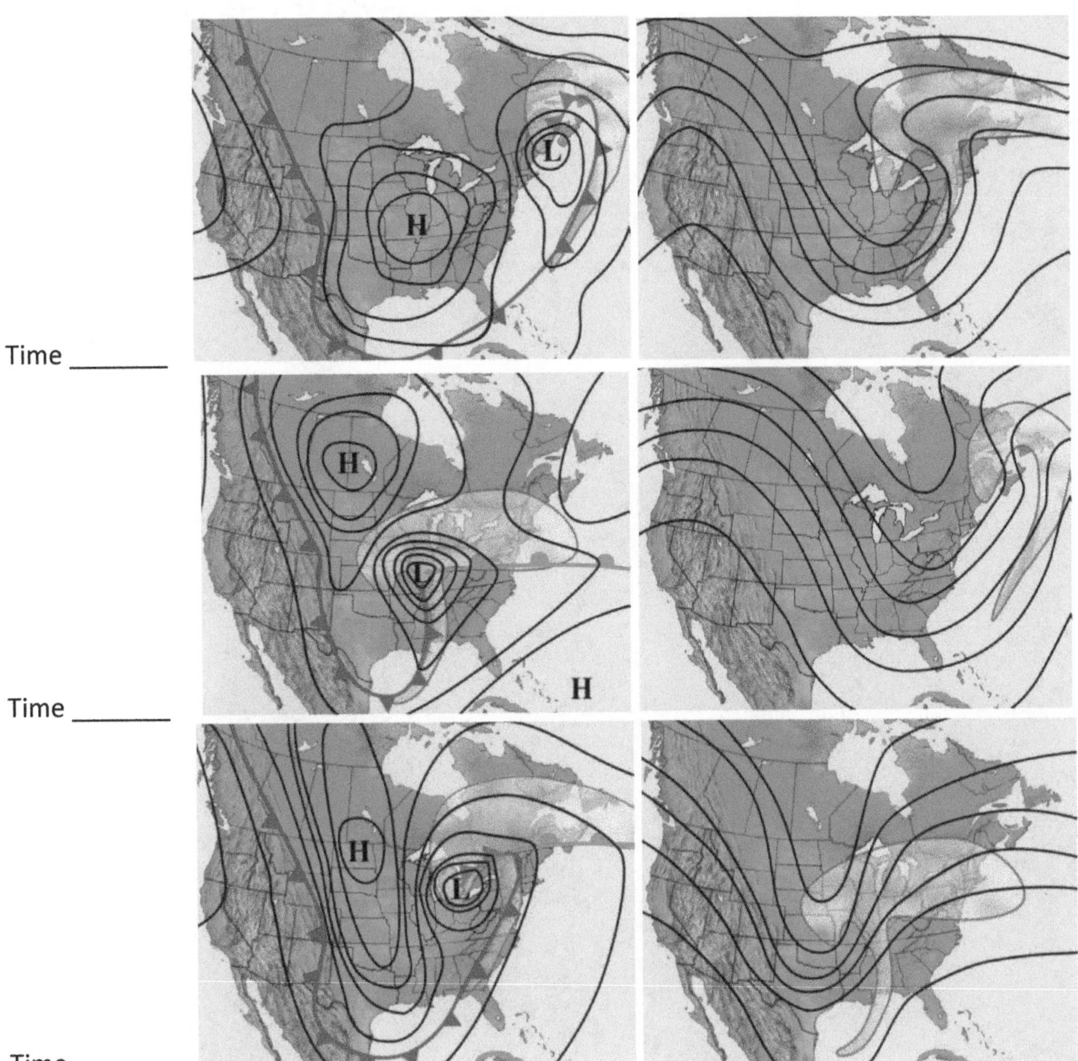

Name: ______________________________ Class: ___________Date: _________

Exercise 14.3 – Cold Waves in North America

Select the word or phrase that best makes each statement true.

1. Airmass cooling is enhanced by (long, short) nights.

2. The core of an arctic airmass is typically (1 to 2 km, 5 to 6 km) deep.

3. Snow cover acts to (reflect, absorb) incoming solar radiation during a cold wave.

4. Cooling the air in the lower troposphere leads to (higher, lower) surface pressure

5. Air found over the Arctic Ocean during winter is typically (warmer, colder) than air over Canada.

6. The low-level airmass in a cold wave is "steered" by winds (at the surface, in the middle troposphere).

7. As cold air moves southward into the United States it is (channeled, warmed) by the Rocky Mountains.

8. Just prior to a cold wave in the United States a (trough, ridge) is present over western North America.

9. A cold wave in the central United States typically occurs just (before, after) the passage of a surface cyclone.

10. The geographic region in the United States most adversely affected by cold waves is the (Northern Plains, Gulf Coast states).

11. Polar airmasses often have a temperature inversion present in the (middle troposphere, lowest several hundred meters).

12. It typically takes a couple (days, weeks) for cold air to move southward across the United States during a severe cold wave.

13. The core of a cold wave at the surface is a strong (high pressure, low pressure) center that forms during winter in high latitudes.

14. Because subsidence occurs in the air associated with cold waves, the temperature of the air when it reaches the central United States is (warmer, colder) than where the airmass originated.

Name: ______________________________ Class: __________Date: _________

Exercise 15.1 – Packing the Car for a Blizzard

Being prepared for a blizzard or blizzard-like conditions is important when you are traveling in winter. List as many essential items as you can think of that you should have in your car in case you become stuck on the side of the road in a blizzard.

1. ______________________________

2. ______________________________

3. ______________________________

4. ______________________________

5. ______________________________

6. ______________________________

7. ______________________________

8. ______________________________

9. ______________________________

10. ______________________________

Name: ______________________________ Class: ___________Date: _________

Exercise 15.2 – Blizzard Facts

Circle the correct answer in each statement:

1. If caught on the side of a road in your car in a white-out blizzard, you should (place flares at distances of 25, 50, and 100 yards from your car; stay in your car).
2. Ground blizzards are caused by (blowing and drifting; falling) snow.
3. The "Winter of Blizzards" in 2019 was followed by (a significant flooding; a large tornado outbreak).
4. In Rocky Mountain cyclones, blizzards occur under the (comma-head; cold front) part of the comma cloud.
5. Blizzards associated with Alberta Clippers typically produce (less; more) snow than blizzards associated with cyclones that form east of the Colorado Rockies.
6. Blizzards associated with Alberta Clippers typically have (colder; warmer) temperatures than blizzards associated with cyclones that form east of the Colorado Rockies.
7. In a blizzard, it is likely that exposed skin will feel (warmer; colder) than the wind chill temperature due to melting and evaporation of snow and water on the skin.
8. The National Weather Service (does; does not) use specific temperature criteria to define a blizzard.
9. A "Blizzard Warning" is issued when winds are expected to exceed (15 knots; 30 knots) and falling or blowing snow is expected to reduce visibility to less than a quarter mile for 3 hours.
10. Blizzards in the lower 48 United States occur most often in (North Dakota; Michigan).

Name: ______________________________ Class: ___________Date: _________

Exercise 15.3 – Which Type of Blizzard?

Descriptions of blizzard conditions experienced by people who were driving west through North Dakota on Interstate 94 are given below. In each case, identify whether the blizzard described was a *Ground Blizzard*, a blizzard associated with an *Alberta Clipper*, or a blizzard associated with a *Colorado Cyclone*. State your reasoning.

1. It was awful. The ground already had 10 inches of snow on it when it started snowing again. The wind picked up and was howling at 40 mph from the north. The snowfall wasn't heavy, but it was blinding. The temperature dropped quickly from 0°F to -20°F. It felt like -50°F! It took us 10 hours to travel only 30 miles. By the time we got there, the radio weather forecaster said 4 inches of additional snow had accumulated. There was really no way to tell because the new snow was fluffy and drifted in huge piles in some locations, with hardly any in other places.

2. We were driving along on I-94 through a town last night. I could see the moon overhead. Suddenly the visibility dropped to zero. Snow was blowing everywhere. I hit the brakes just in time to keep from crashing into a truck that was pulling off the road. I went on at about 15 mph for a few miles. Just as fast as the snow started, it stopped. About 10 minutes later, it happened again. This went on half way across the state, and added several hours to my driving time.

3. Rain was falling when we crossed the Minnesota/North Dakota border heading west. Within 20 miles the temperature dropped from 36°F to 10°F. At first the snow was light, but then it started really coming down. The snow became so heavy I couldn't see more than a few feet in front of my car. Then, the temperature dropped and winds picked up to about 50 mph. It was snowing horizontally! We managed to get to the next exit, only to find the interstate closed. We had no choice but to stay in a motel and wait it out. In the morning everything was covered with at least a foot of snow and drifts were over 5 feet high. It took the highway maintenance crews three days to open the Interstate.

Name: ______________________________ Class: ___________Date: _________

Exercise 15.4 – Where is the Blizzard?

The map below shows a cyclone over the central United States. Assume it is midwinter and a severe blizzard is occurring.

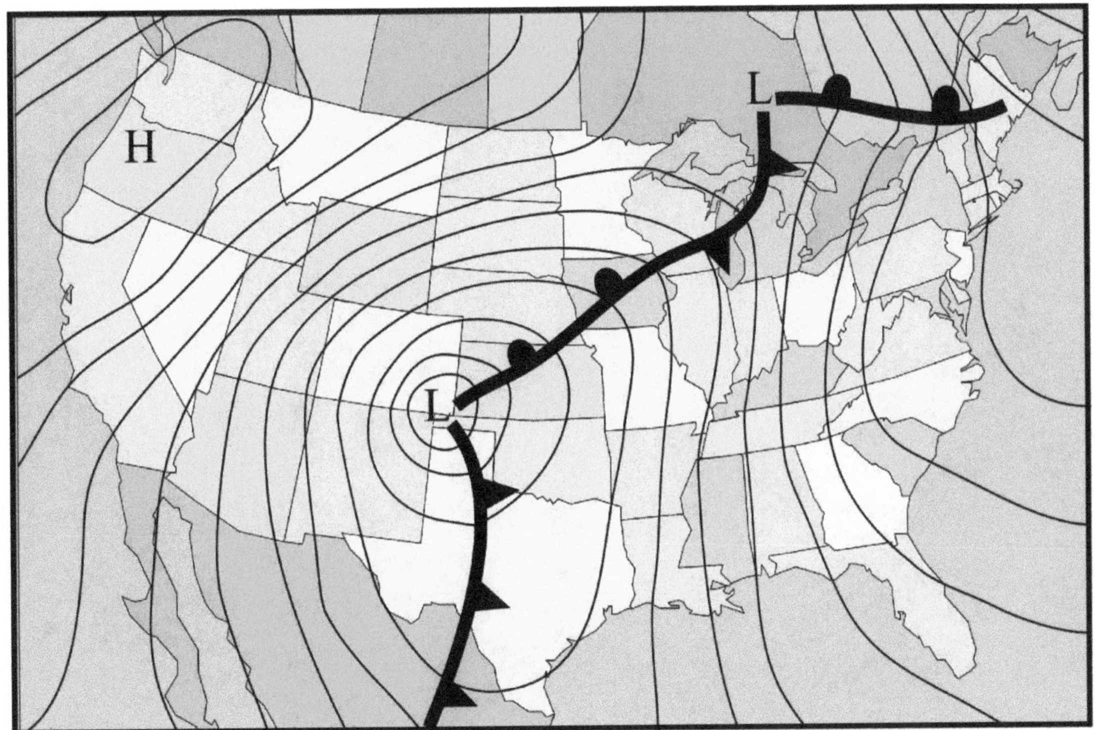

1. Shade in the region of the United States and/or Canada that would be most likely to be experiencing blizzard conditions at the time of the map.

2. What information did you use to determine where the blizzard would be?

3. Is this system an example of an Alberta Clipper? How do you know?

Name: ______________________________ Class: ___________ Date: __________

Exercise 16.1 – Western U.S. Mountain Geography

Draw a line on the map to indicate the location of each of the mountain ranges listed. Label each line. In the space provided, list the states in which the mountain ranges are found.

<u>Mountain Range</u>	<u>States in U.S.</u>
Cascades	______________________________
Sierra Nevada	______________________________
Coast Range	______________________________
Wasatch Range	______________________________
Bitterroot Mountains	______________________________
Rocky Mountains	______________________________

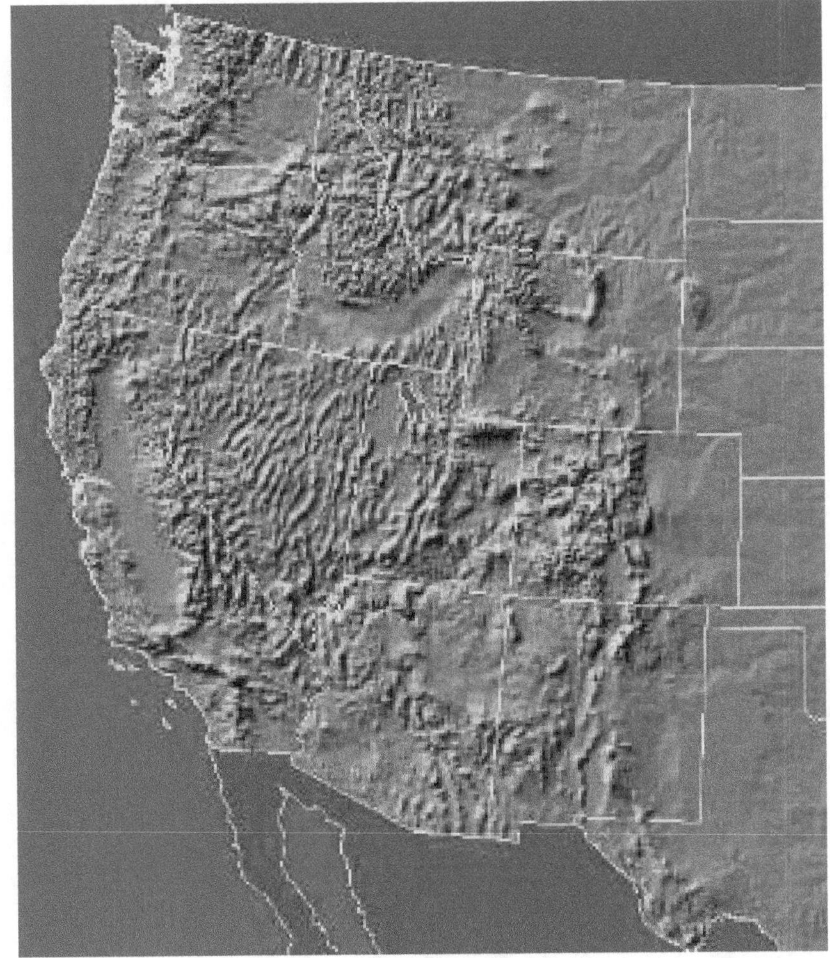

Name: ______________________________ Class: ___________Date: _________

Exercise 16.2 – Pressure Patterns, Wind Flow, and Mountain Snows

The four surface maps below each show the sea level pressure distribution across the western United States on different days in January.

1. Draw arrows around the pressure systems to indicate wind direction. (The first one is done for you.)
2. Shade in the regions on each map where the wind direction is favorable for the development of snow in the mountains of the western United States.
3. If the snow would fall on the east slope of the Rockies, label it "upslope snow."

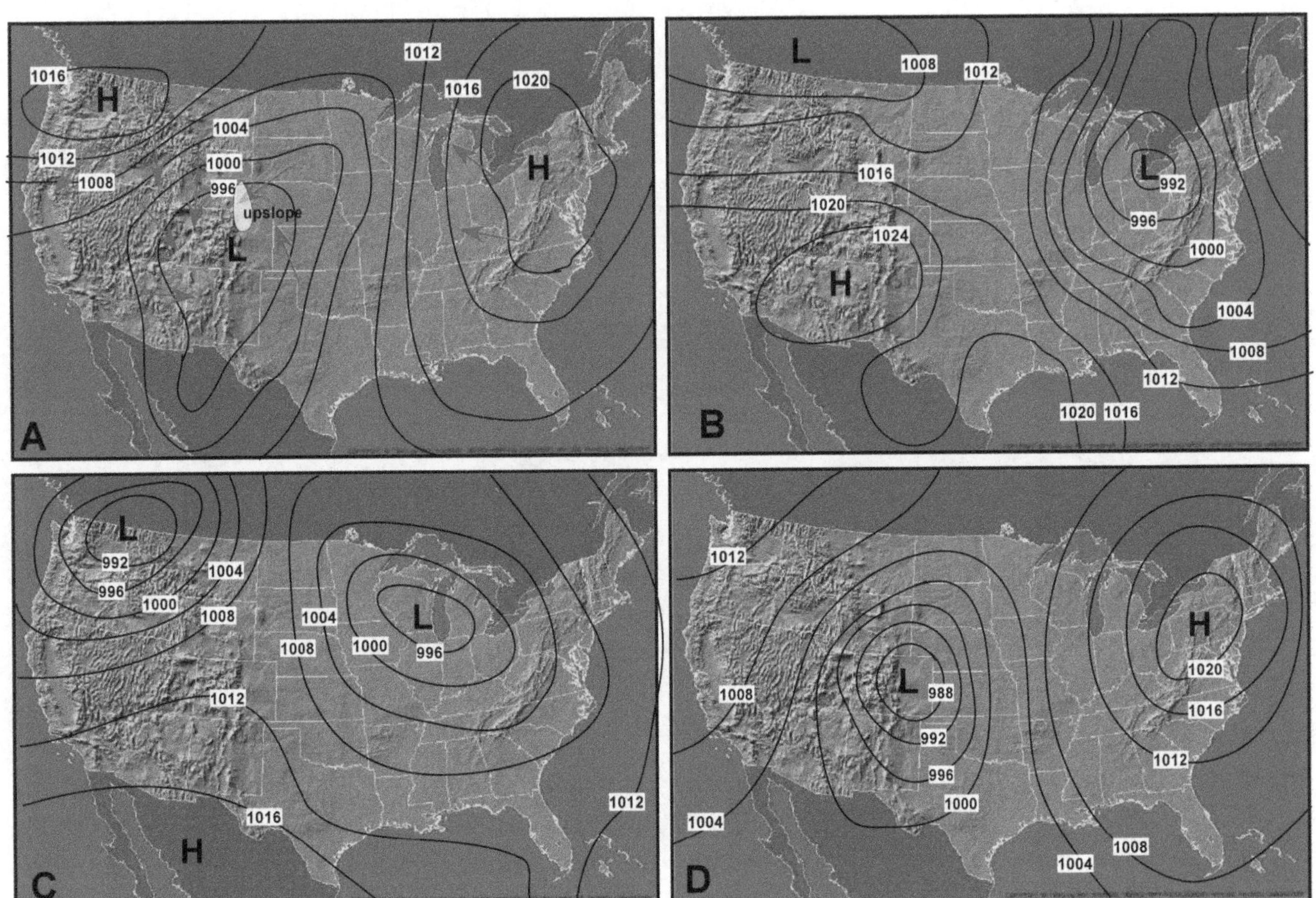

Name: ______________________________ Class: ___________Date: __________

Exercise 16.3 – Impacts of Mountain Snowstorms

Determine if each statement is "True" or "False."

1. T F Water from mountain snowstorms provides about a third of the electricity throughout the western United States and over 80 percent in Oregon and Washington.

2. T F Fatalities associated with avalanches in the United States have been decreasing in recent years because of better warning systems.

3. T F The strategy used by cloud seeding operations is to convert supercooled water in the clouds to ice crystals. They do this because ice crystals grow at the expense of liquid drops.

4. T F The primary reason that mountains experience so many snowstorms in a winter season is that deep cumulonimbus clouds develop over the mountains nearly every day due to heating of the slopes during daytime.

5. T F Many locations along the Sierra Nevada and Cascades receive 20 to 30 feet (240 to 360 inches) of snow during a year with average snowfall.

6. T F The Chain Law refers to the chains that are used to block roads during potential avalanches. Drivers are not permitted to take their cars across the chains.

7. T F The water-equivalent of snow in the mountains can range from 4 inches of snow to one inch of water, to 30 inches of snow per inch of water.

8. T F Upslope storms on the east slope of the Colorado Rockies are important because they affect a population corridor that includes the cities of Omaha, Nebraska, and Kansas City, Kansas.

9. T F The weather pattern most conducive to an upslope storm along the east slope of the Colorado Rockies is one in which there is a low pressure system to the north of Colorado and a high pressure system to the south of Colorado.

10. T F The city of Denver has the best chance of a heavy snowstorm when the surface winds in winter are blowing from the northeast.

11. T F A high pressure system to the west of a mountain range will favor snow on the east slopes of the mountain range.

12. T F If recent patterns of climate change continue, in the future less snow will fall on the lower elevations of the major mountain ranges of the West.

Name: ______________________________ Class: ___________Date: _________

Exercise 17.1 – Characteristics of Mountain Windstorms

Identify the type of mountain windstorm described in each statement by putting the appropriate letter on the blank provided. If the description has more than one correct answer, list all the correct answers on the blank.

C – Chinook
S – Santa Ana
K – Katabatic wind

________ 1. Commonly found on the eastern slopes of the Rocky Mountains.

________ 2. Found in Greenland and Antarctica.

________ 3. Can be very strong, with wind gusts exceeding 100 knots.

________ 4. Found in southern California.

________ 5. Turbulent winds often carry loose snow and create ground blizzards.

________ 6. Most common during autumn.

________ 7. Can be warm and dry wind similar to an Alpine Foehn or cold and dry, similar to a Bora.

________ 8. Caused by cold air that initially develops on top of an elevated landmass.

________ 9. Can cause significant damage by spreading wildfires that occur typically in autumn.

________ 10. Can develop when a strong high-pressure system forms over the Great Basin.

________ 11. Is capable of quickly melting ice and snow at the base of the mountains.

________ 12. Winds are always cold in spite of adiabatic warming during descent.

________ 13. Is a downslope windstorm.

________ 14. Can raise the air temperature as much as 15°C (27°F)

________ 15. These windstorms occur approximately 20 days per year and each event lasts an average of one and one half days.

________ 16. Is driven by a strong pressure gradient.

Name: ______________________________ Class: ___________Date: _________

Exercise 17.2 – Foehn or Bora?

When the *Foehn* blows down the north side of the Alps in Switzerland, the *temperature abruptly warms* as cold air is flushed out of the Alpine valleys and replaced with the warm air that descended the mountains. When the *Bora* blows down the south side of the Dinaric Alps of Serbia, the *temperature* on the Mediterranean side abruptly *drops*.

In the United States, temperature changes like the Foehn and Bora can be experienced during downslope windstorms east of the Rockies. The figures below show 3 different temperature conditions prior to the onset a downslope windstorm. Assume in each case that the airmass at the base of the mountain (light shading) will be forced eastward by air descending the mountain from mountaintop. Determine the temperature change of air that descends from the mountaintop to the base, and circle whether the temperature change is similar to a Foehn or Bora.

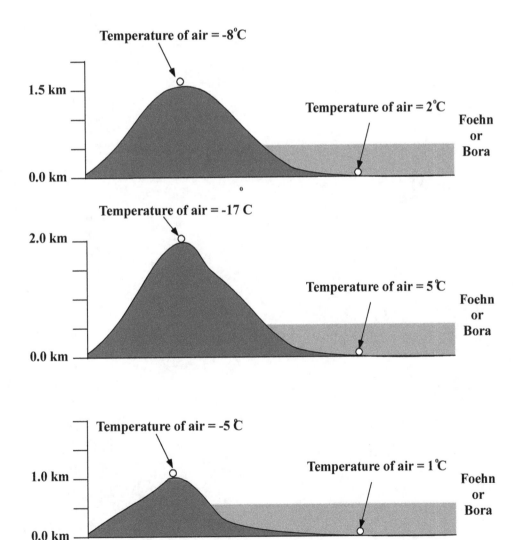

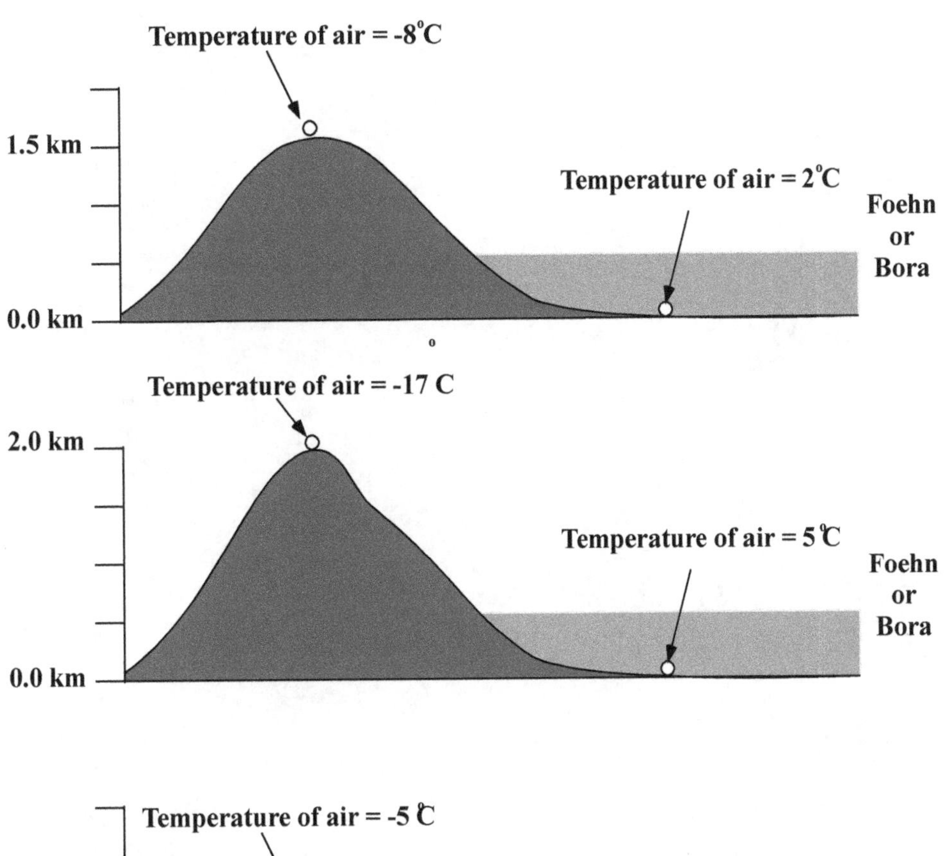

Name: ______________________________ Class: ___________Date: _________

Exercise 17.3 – Features of a Downslope Windstorm

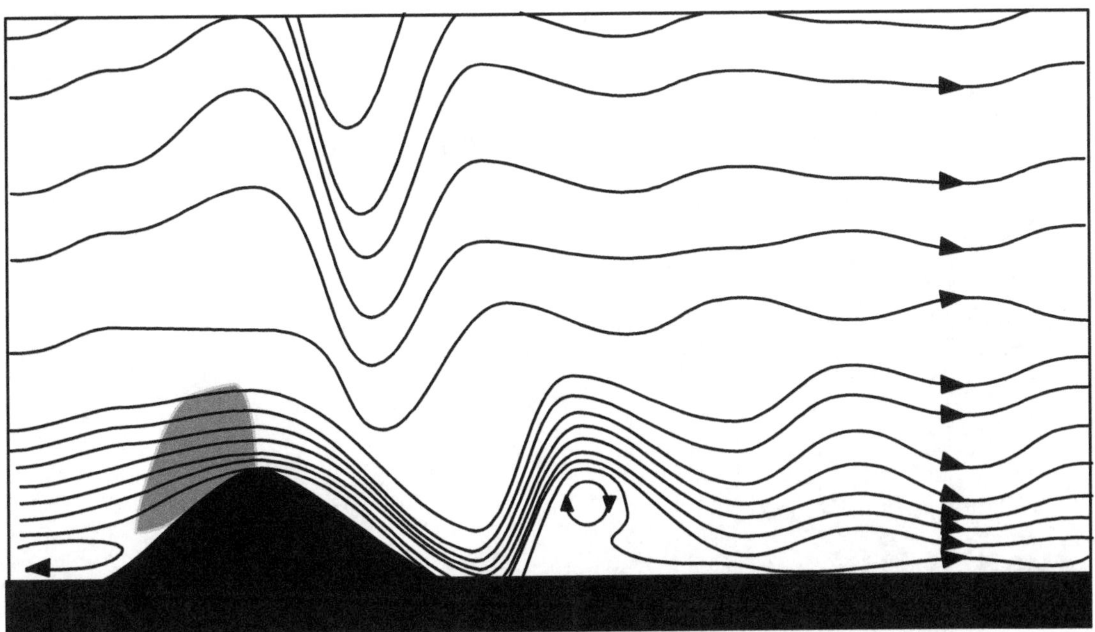

The diagram above is a cross section through a mountain range looking west to east. The contours shown are streamlines of wind flow. A downslope windstorm is occurring. The gray shaded region indicates the location of clouds. On the diagram, place letters where the features listed below are located:

A. Chinook Wall

B. Rotor

C. Hydraulic Jump

D. Breaking waves

E. Inversion

F. Most severe winds at surface

G. Shooting flow

H. Snowstorm

Name: ______________________________ Class: ___________Date: _________

Exercise 18.1 – Characteristics of Thunderstorms

Identify the type of thunderstorm described in each statement.

OT	ordinary thunderstorm
MCS	mesoscale convective systems
FSL	frontal squall lines
SP	supercell
ALL	true for all four thunderstorm types

________ 1. Always rotate

________ 2. Occur in clusters

________ 3. Contain thunder and lightning

OT______ 4. Rarely produce severe conditions

________ 5. Form far from frontal boundaries

________ 6. Form in regions with weak or no wind shear

________ 7. Appear as a hook shaped echo on radar reflectivity

________ 8. Commonly form along the "tail of the comma cloud"

________ 9. Appear as a long continuous line on radar reflectivity

________ 10. Account for most large, damaging tornadoes and large hail

________ 11. Responsible for much of the summer rainfall in the Central Plains

________ 12. The anvil can grow to cover an area the size of an entire U.S state

________ 13. Have an anvil and may have mammatus on the underside of the anvil

________ 14. Can produce hail and tornadoes but are most often associated with strong straight line winds

________ 15. A low-level jet helps transport warm moist air into the storm and provides low-level wind shear that contributes to storm rotation

Name: ______________________________ Class: ___________Date: _________

Exercise 18.2 – Thunderstorm Features

While there are ways that thunderstorms organize, all thunderstorms have many structural features in common. Identify the thunderstorm feature described in each of the following from the list provided.

A – anvil	M – mammatus clouds
C – cold pool	O – overshooting top
D – downdraft	S – shelf cloud (or roll cloud depending on shape)
E – entrainment	T – tropopause
G – gust front	U – updraft

1. ______ Warm, buoyant plume of rising air
2. ______ Accumulation of rain-cooled air near the surface
3. ______ A bulge at the cloud top produced by strong updrafts
4. ______ Dry air mixing in from the sides and top of the cloud
5. ______ If air is sufficiently buoyant it will rise to this altitude
6. ______ Forms when air from the updraft exhausts horizontally at the tropopause
7. ______ Forms via falling precipitation and is enhanced by evaporation of precipitation
8. ______ Typically forms over the gust front as warm air is lifted over the spreading cold pool
9. ______ Forms at the base of thunderstorm anvils and appear like rounded "bags" hanging from the anvil
10. ______ Created when cool air, generated by evaporation of rain within downdrafts, spreads outward away from the thunderstorm after reaching the surface

Name: ______________________________ Class: __________Date: _________

Exercise 18.3 – Thunderstorm Sizes

On each of the four maps below, for the type of thunderstorm listed:

1. Sketch the approximate size of the cloud shield that would be observed by a satellite.
2. Within the cloud shield you drew, sketch the approximate size of the precipitation region, as would be observed with radar.

Ordinary Thunderstorm

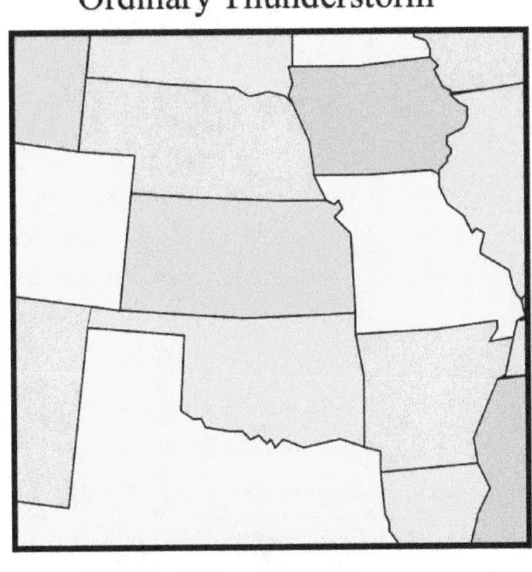

Mesoscale Convective System

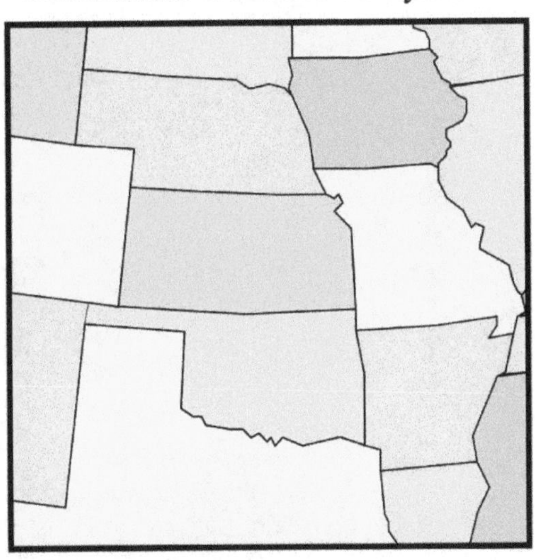

Frontal Squall Line

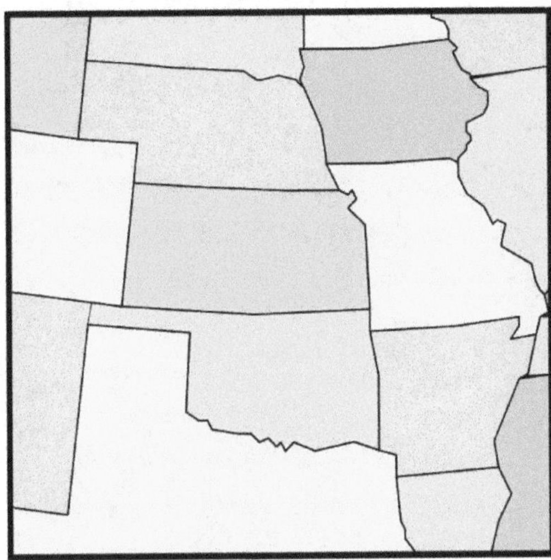

Supercell Thunderstorm

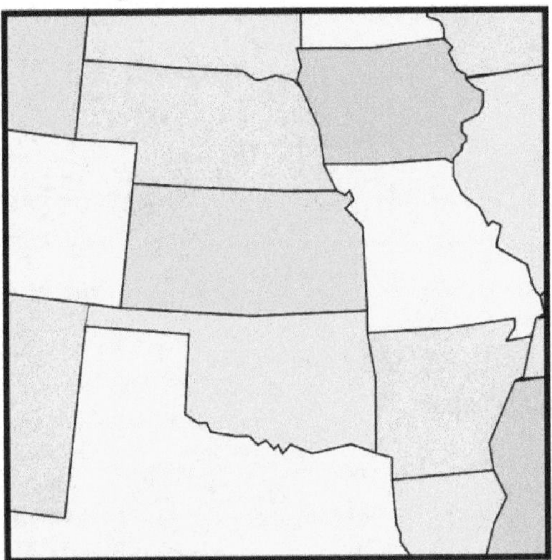

Name: ______________________ Class: __________ Date: _________

Exercise 18.4 – Squall Line Structure

1. In the two boxes labeled "region" on the diagram below, place an "S" in the box in the stratiform region and a "C" in the box in the convective region.
2. Beneath the ground level of the diagram, place an "L" in the box where lighter rainfall occurs and an "H" in the box where heavy rainfall is typically found. Place a "U" in the box closest to the base of the updraft.
3. Label the following features by placing the letter in the appropriate box to indicate the location.

A – rear inflow jet

B – mammatus

C –forward anvil

D – overshooting top

E – shelf cloud

F – tropopause

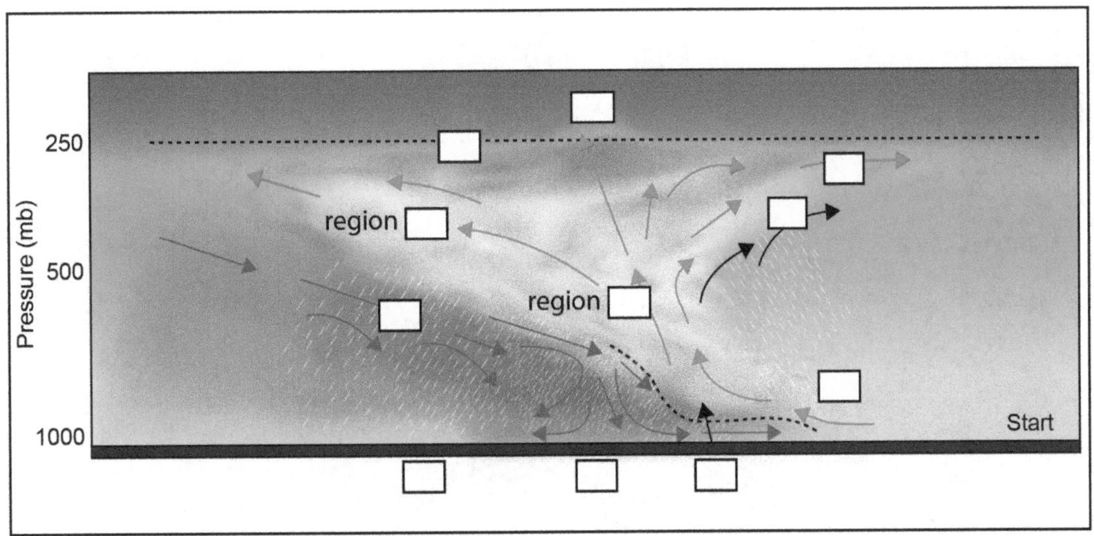

4. Supposed you were in a car at a position labeled "Start" and you drove through the storm (from right to left on the diagram). Describe briefly what you would experience in terms of wind, rain and lightning as you drove through the storm.

Name: ______________________________ Class: ___________Date: __________

Exercise 18.5 – Supercell Thunderstorm Structure

Identify the structural features of a supercell thunderstorm by placing the corresponding letter at the appropriate location on the diagram.

A – anvil

B – bounded weak echo region

C – heavy rain

D –large hail

E – light rain

F – mammatus

G – moderate rain region

H – rain / hail mix

I – overshooting top

J – rear flanking line

K – small hail

L – tornado

M – tropopause

N – virga

O – wall cloud

P – backsheared anvil

Q – forward flank downdraft

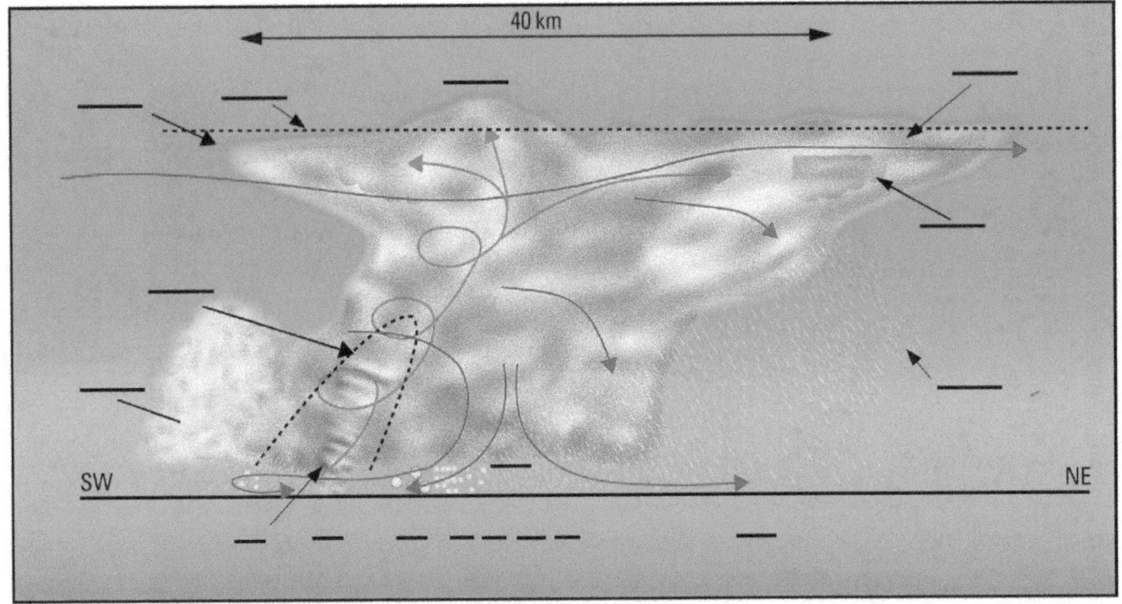

Name [illegible] Date [illegible]

Exercise 13.5 [illegible] thunderstorm [illegible]

Identify the structural features of a supercell thunderstorm [illegible] at the appropriate location [illegible]

A [illegible]

B [illegible]

C [illegible]

D [illegible]

[illegible]

Name: ______________________________ Class: ___________ Date: _________

Exercise 19.1 – Tornado: Myth or Fact?

Indicate whether each of the following statements about tornadoes is *fact* or *myth.*

1.	Tornadoes can be invisible.	MYTH	FACT
2.	Tornadoes have occurred in all 50 states.	MYTH	FACT
3.	Tornadoes are attracted to mobile home communities.	MYTH	FACT
4.	Tornadoes always rotate counter-clockwise in the Northern Hemisphere.	MYTH	FACT
5.	If a tornado watch has been issued, then this means a tornado has been sighted.	MYTH	FACT
6.	Tornadoes cannot hit downtown areas because the buildings deflect the airflow.	MYTH	FACT
7.	If there is a tornado watch, you should open all the windows in your house or apartment.	MYTH	FACT
8.	A tornado can contain within its circulation two or more smaller vortices called suction vortices.	MYTH	FACT
9.	An interior room of a building with no windows is one of the safer places to be during a tornado.	MYTH	FACT
10.	When the tornado siren goes off you should grab your camera and go outside to record the event.	MYTH	FACT
11.	If you are driving in a car on the highway and see a tornado behind you, seeing an overpass and hiding under it is not a safe course of action.	MYTH	FACT
12.	When the tornado siren goes off, go to the innermost room in the lowest level of your house or building.	MYTH	FACT
13.	If your area is under a tornado watch the safest course of action is to grab your camera phone, jump in the car and chase it.	MYTH	FACT
14.	If you have no basement, during a tornado seek shelter in a ground floor level bathroom, get in the bathtub and cover yourself with a blanket to protect from flying debris.	MYTH	FACT

Name: ______________________________ Class: ___________Date: _________

Exercise 19.2 – Tornado Wind Speeds

Assume that a tornado is on the ground but has no forward speed. Using the principle of conservation of angular momentum, estimate the wind speeds of the tornado based on the measured rotation of the winds in the mesocyclone. Use the space to the right of each problem to work through the math. (1 mile=5280 ft)

Conservation of angular momentum relates the rotational velocity, v, to the radial distance, r, from the center of rotation:

$$r_{(mesocyclone)} * v_{(mesocyclone)} = r_{(tornado)} * v_{(tornado)}$$

1. radius of mesocyclone = 5 miles
   rotational velocity of mesocyclone = 5 mph
   radius of tornado = 1742 ft
   rotational velocity of tornado = _____________

2. radius of mesocyclone = 4 miles
   rotational velocity of mesocyclone = 3 mph
   radius of tornado = 528 ft
   rotational velocity of tornado = _____________

3. *diameter* of mesocyclone = 10 miles
   rotational velocity of mesocyclone = 6 mph
   radius of tornado = 528 ft
   rotational velocity of tornado = _____________

Name: ______________________________ Class: ____________Date: __________

Exercise 19.3 – Tornado-Like Vortices

Identify the vortex (or vortices) described in each of the statements below by choosing from the list provided.

CAF – cold air funnels
DD – dust devils
GN – gustnadoes
LS – landspouts
WS – waterspouts
ALL – all of the above

_______ 1. Rarely reach the ground.

_______ 2. Are typically very weak and short-lived

_______ 3. Most tornadoes in California are this type.

_______ 4. Do not display a hook shaped echo on radar reflectivity displays.

_______ 5. Are most commonly observed off coastlines in tropical regions.

_______ 6. Are weak, short-lived and are associated with dry convection.

_______ 7. Develop along fronts that have strong horizontal wind shear.

_______ 8. Sometimes several form every few kilometers along a front.

_______ 9. Emerge from convective clouds that develop over cool surface air.

_______ 10. Develop at the base of cumulus cloud associated with a cutoff low.

_______ 11. Forms along the boundary of cool outflow ahead of a thunderstorm.

_______ 12. Most common over the desert region of the southwestern United States.

_______ 13. Emerge from the base of elevated convective clouds that develop over cool surface air.

Name: ______________________________ Class: ___________ Date: _________

Exercise 19.4 – Probability of Experiencing a Tornado

Suppose that the National Weather Service issues a tornado watch for an area containing your location. Assume a typical size of a tornado "watch box" is 100 miles × 200 miles.

1. Suppose that a single tornado actually occurs within this watch box area. What is your probability of being struck by the tornado in each of the following scenarios of tornado occurrence?

	F rating	*length of path*	*width of path*	*probability of being struck*
(a)	F1	2 mi.	0.1 mi.	_______
(b)	F2	5 mi.	0.2 mi.	_______
(c)	F3	10 mi.	0.25 mi.	_______
(d)	F4	20 mi.	0.3 mi.	_______
(e)	F5	40 mi.	0.4 mi.	_______

2. What is the probability that you would be within 25 miles of a tornado if one tornado occurred in the watch box?

3. Suppose that the EF5 tornado in (1) only had EF5 winds for 1 mile of its path length and only on the right half of the damage path. What is the probability that you would be struck by the tornado with full EF5 intensity?

Name: ______________________________ Class: ___________Date: __________

Exercise 20.1 – Hailstone Sizes

Idealized cross-sections of different sized hailstones, drawn to scale, are shown below. Identify the hailstone as: pea, marble, quarter, golf ball or tennis ball sized; record the approximate diameter of each in centimeters and inches; and estimate the number of supercooled droplets that are contained in each hailstone. Assume the diameter of a supercooled droplet is 0.2 millimeters. The volume of a sphere is $V = 4/3\ \pi\ r^3$ or $1/6\ \pi\ d^3$, where $\pi = 3.14$, r is radius, and d is diameter.

1

2

3

4

5

	Size Descriptor	Diameter cm	Diameter in	# of Supercooled Droplets
1.				
2.				
3.				
4.				
5.				

Name: ______________________________ Class: ___________Date: __________

Exercise 20.2 – Hail Distribution in Thunderstorms

The diagram below is a plan view of radar reflectivity from a supercell thunderstorm. Suppose that three cars drive through the thunderstorm along transects AA', BB' and CC', starting in each case at the unprimed letter.

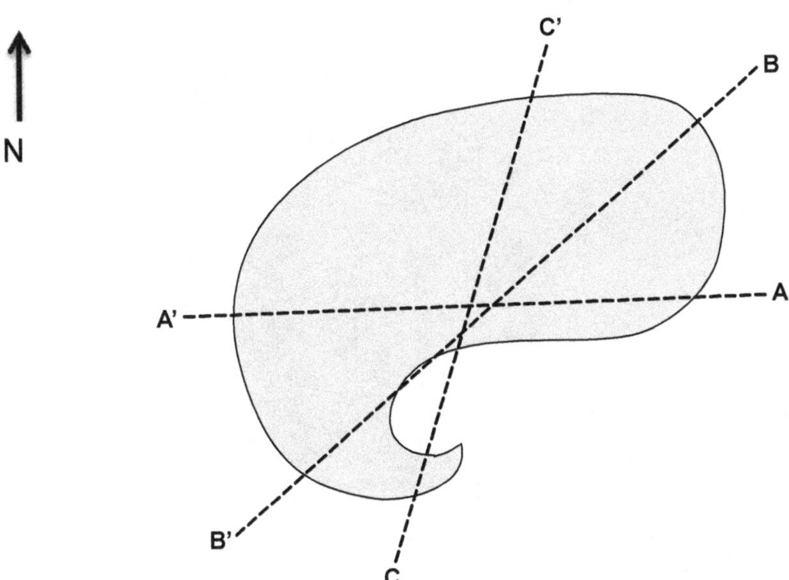

1. List the precipitation types the driver would likely encounter on each route, in the order they would appear along the route.

A____A'

B____B'

C____C'

2. Place an "X" on each transect in the diagram at the location where each car is in the greatest danger of experiencing hail damage.

Name: ______________________________ Class: __________Date: _________

Exercise 20.3 – Polarization Diversity Radars and Hail Detection

Polarization diversity radars measure both reflectivity and differential reflectivity. The magnitude of the reflectivity is related to the size and number of raindrops and hailstones intercepted by the radar beam, while the differential reflectivity is related to the shape of the raindrops and hailstones.

Very small raindrops and cloud droplets are spherical. On average, most hailstones are nearly spherical. For these near-spherical objects, the differential reflectivity is between 0 to 1 decibels. Large raindrops flatten as they fall into shapes resembling hamburger buns. For large raindrops, the differential reflectivity is about 1 to 3 decibels.

The reflectivity has low values (10 to 20 dBZ) in parts of the storm containing very small water droplets, moderate values (20 to 40 dBZ) in parts of the storm containing rain, and high values (40 to 60 dBZ) in parts of the storm that may either have heavy rain or hail.

Used together, the reflectivity and the differential reflectivity can be used to isolate parts of storms containing only hail. The cross sections below show the reflectivity and differential reflectivity measured in the bottom half of a supercell thunderstorm. Using the criteria above, draw a line (on each diagram) enclosing the region that is likely to contain hail. In the space below the diagram, state your reasoning.

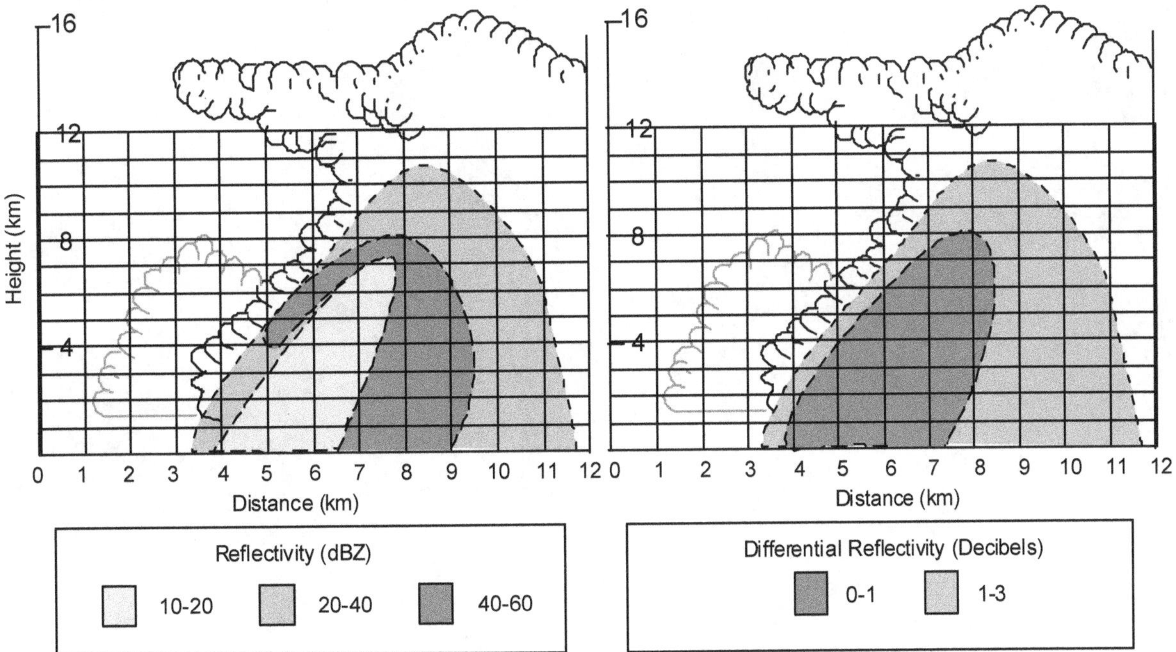

Name: ______________________________ Class: ___________ Date: _________

Exercise 20.4 – Hailstreaks and Hailswaths

The white regions on the diagrams below show hailstreaks that occurred during two severe thunderstorm outbreaks. For each example, outline the hailswaths and complete the table below.

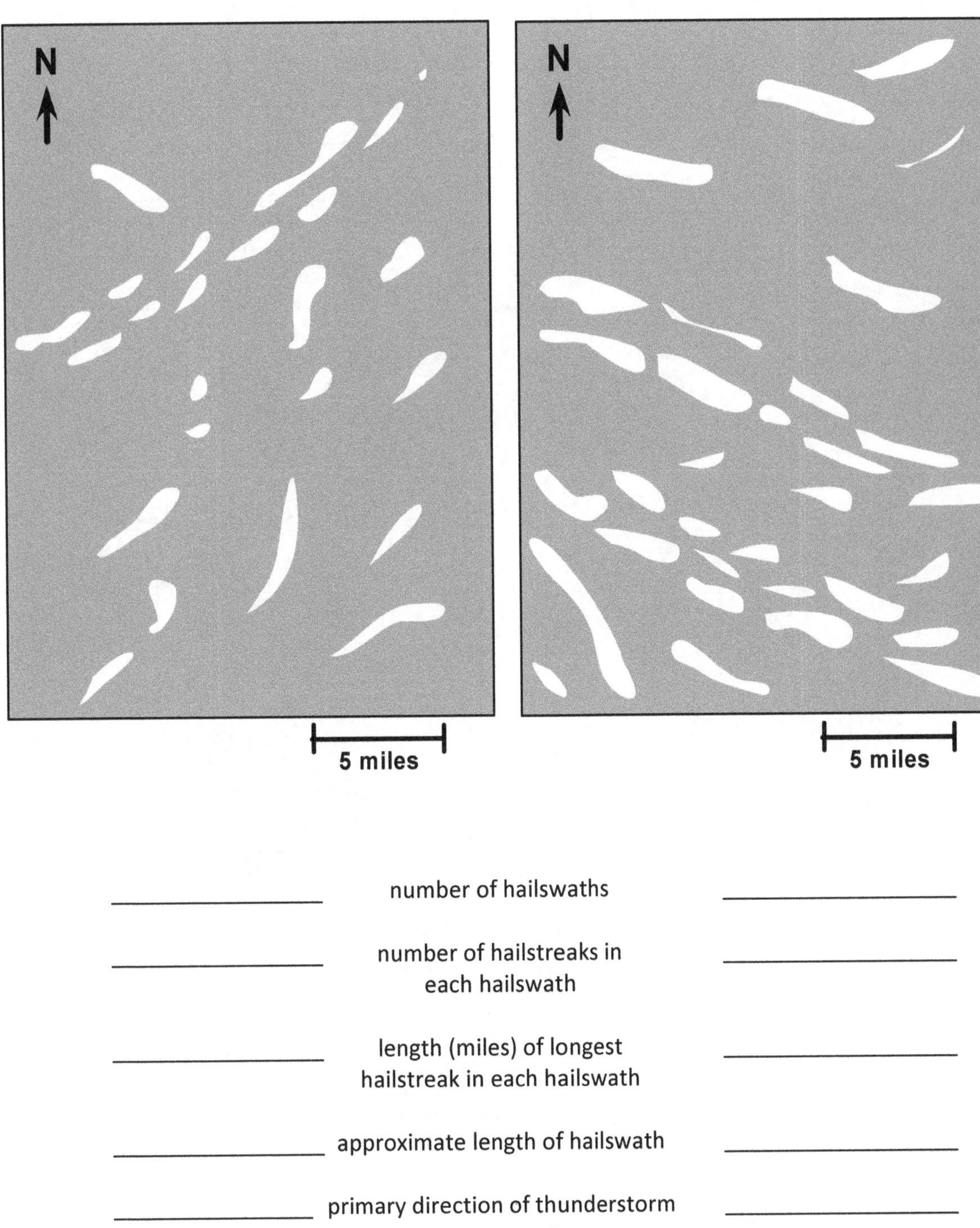

______________	number of hailswaths	______________
______________	number of hailstreaks in each hailswath	______________
______________	length (miles) of longest hailstreak in each hailswath	______________
______________	approximate length of hailswath	______________
______________	primary direction of thunderstorm movement	______________

Name: ______________________________ Class: ___________Date: _________

Exercise 21.1 – Lightning: Myth or Fact?

Determine whether each of the statements below is myth or fact with regard to lightning and lightning safety.

1. Lightning is not always associated with thunder. MYTH FACT
2. Lightning never strikes the same place twice. MYTH FACT
3. The risk of a person in the U.S. being struck by lightning is approximately 1 in 280,000 per year. MYTH FACT
4. If you are caught outdoors during an electrical storm one of the safest places to be is in your car. MYTH FACT
5. If it is not raining there is no danger from lightning. MYTH FACT
6. The rubber soles of shoes will protect you from harm if struck by lightning. MYTH FACT
7. People struck by lightning carry an electrical charge and should not be touched. MYTH FACT
8. "Heat lightning" occurs after very hot summer days and poses no threat to anyone when it occurs. MYTH FACT
9. A lightning stroke heats the air to a temperature five times the temperature of the sun's surface. MYTH FACT
10. Locations of lightning strokes can be predicted. MYTH FACT
11. A typical lightning stroke is 5 kilometers long and 2 to 3 centimeters wide. MYTH FACT
12. It is unsafe to be indoors near appliances or plumbing during a lightning event. MYTH FACT
13. If you feel your hair stand on end during a storm, crouch down low to the ground – you could be struck by lightning! MYTH FACT

Name: ______________________________ Class: ___________Date: _________

Exercise 21.2 – Lightning Phenomena

Match the statements to the types of lightning phenomena listed below. Some answers can be used more than once.

Heat lightning
Bead lightning
Sheet lightning
St. Elmo's Fire
Red sprites
Blue jets
Elves
Ball lightning
Positive polarity lightning
Stepped leader

____________________ 1. Illuminates a cloud uniformly.

____________________ 2. Sparks that occur on metal objects.

____________________ 3. Lightning from the anvil region of a thunderstorm.

____________________ 4. Disk-shaped regions of light found far above a thunderstorm.

____________________ 5. Originally, people thought that the light was generated by summer heat.

____________________ 6. Floats in air after a lightning strike; ranges in color and may last 30 seconds.

____________________ 7. A bluish-green halo appears at the top of ships masts as continuous sparking occurs.

____________________ 8. Flash of light overhead from a lighting stroke so far in the distance that thunder is not heard.

____________________ 9. Beads of light in a line thought to be caused by the deionization of the lightning channel.

____________________ 10. Earliest part of a lightning discharge in which negative charge begins to descend below cloud base.

____________________ 11. Cannot be detected by the naked eye, but extends in a cone shape from the top of the active part of thunderstorms.

____________________ 12. Lightning stroke breaks into separate, distinct segments of light that do not last long enough to be observed by the human eye.

____________________ 13. Large, weak luminous flashes that emanate upward from the anvil regions of thunderstorms and are brightest at heights of 65 to 75 km.

Name: ______________________________ Class: ___________Date: _________

Exercise 21.3 – Lightning in the United States

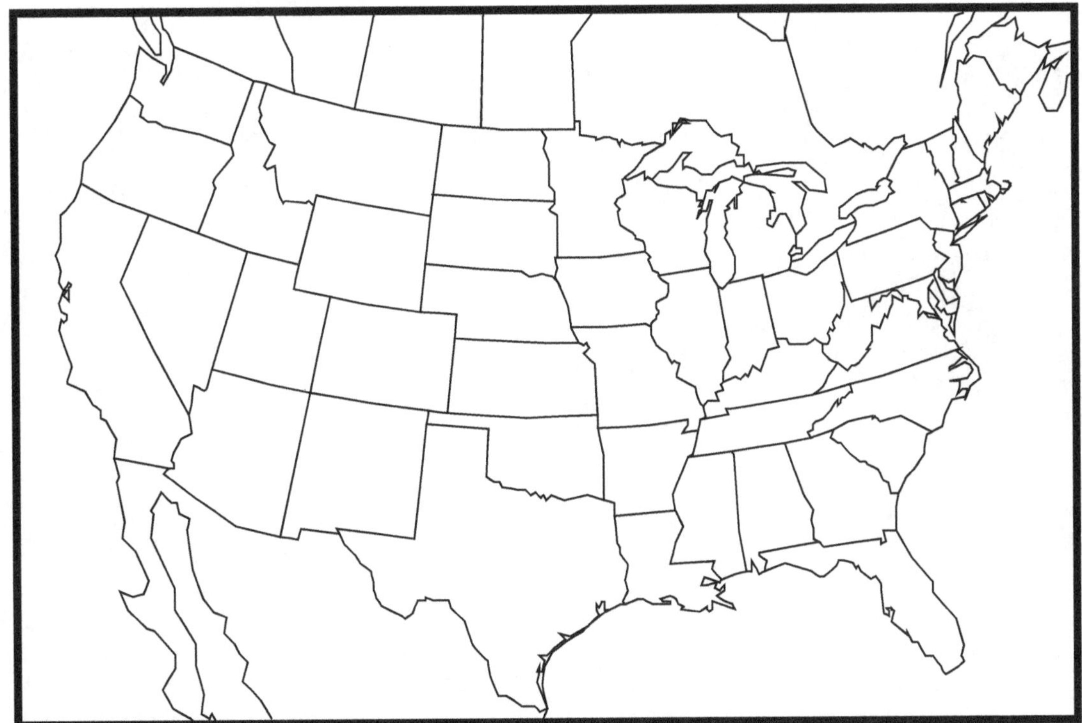

1. You are giving a talk about lightning to a 6th grade class. The teacher of the class brings out the map above and asks you to show the children where in the United States people are in (a) the greatest danger, (b) moderate danger, and (c) the least danger of being stuck by lightning, based on the frequency of lightning. Sketch on the map above your answer to this question.

2. Give the children a simple explanation why lightning is more common in the areas you outlined (write your answer below).

Name: ______________________________ Class: ___________Date: _________

Exercise 21.4 – Lightning Development

A thunderstorm cloud that is in the first stage of development of a lightning discharge is shown in the diagram above.

1. On the diagram, show the distribution of charge within the cloud and at the ground just prior to the lightning stroke. (Use the symbols "+" and "-" for the positive and negative charges, respectively).

2. What is the name given to the descending region of negative just before a lightning strike?

3. Describe briefly the remaining sequence of events that will occur during the lightning discharge.

Name: ______________________________ Class: ____________Date: __________

Exercise 22.1 – Aircraft and Downbursts

The diagram below shows a cross-section through a downburst. The horizontal wind speeds in the diagram are given for four altitudes.

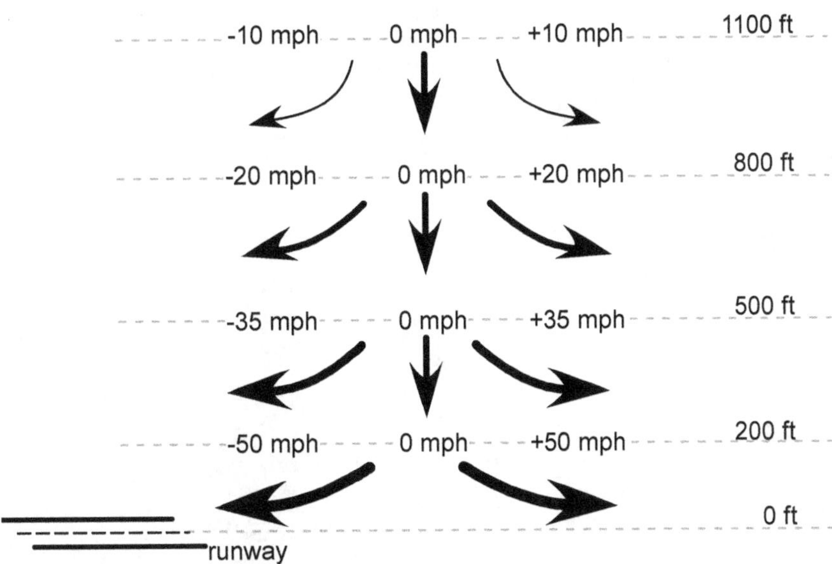

1. A single-engine Cessna plane enters the downburst from the right at an elevation of 500 feet. The plane's air speed in the calm air outside the downburst is 150 mph. Calculate how the airspeed will change as the pilot flies through the downburst. Assume the pilot maintains a ground speed of 150 mph at all times and manages to keep the plane at exactly 500 feet above the earth's surface.

2. Assume instead that the pilot does not maintain a constant altitude, but does maintain a constant ground speed of 150 mph. Sketch on the diagram above a plausible scenario for the plane's altitude as it flies through the downburst.

3. Suppose the same plane enters the downburst from the left instead of the right. How does your answer to (2) change?

4. Suppose the same plane is preparing to land from right to left on the runway shown above. The plane's stall speed is 100 mph. If the plane's ground speed is 130 mph in the calm air to the far right of the downburst and the pilot maintains this speed relative to the ground, how high in the downburst does the plane have to be in order to avoid stall speed in the approach to the runway? What should the pilot do?

Name: ______________________________ Class: ___________Date: __________

Exercise 22.2 – Downburst Indications from Soundings

Compare the soundings in terms of four characteristics of an atmospheric environment conducive to downbursts by completing the table at the bottom of this page. Provide a reason for your choice. Determine which location (sounding A or sounding B) is more likely to experience downbursts.

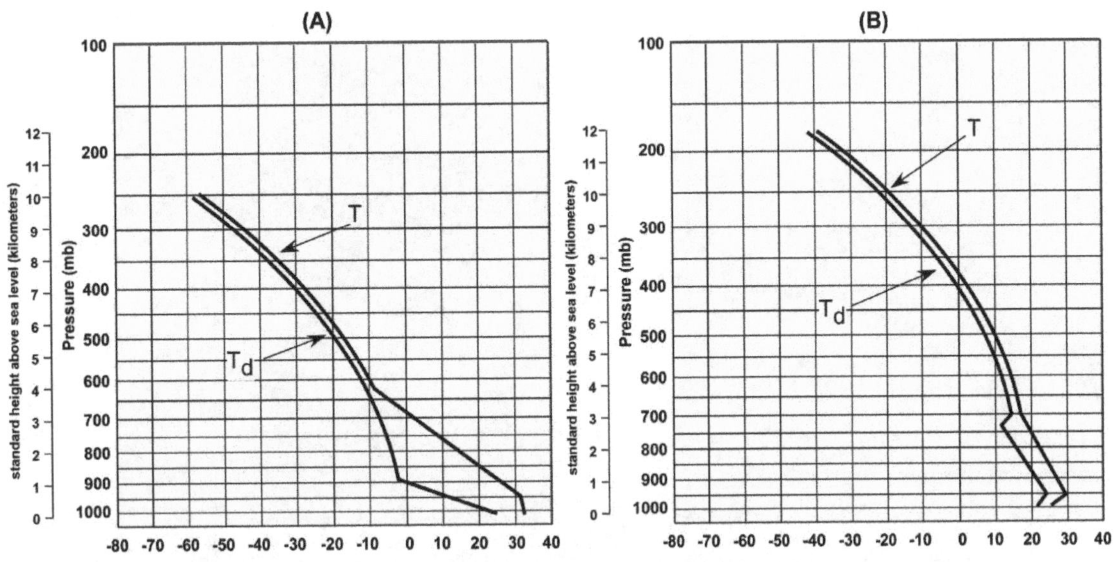

Characteristic	Most favorable (A or B)	Reason
1. Large environmental lapse rate below cloud		
2. Dry air below cloud base		
3. Increase of air's moisture content near surface		
4. Below-freezing in much of cloud		

Downburst is most likely at: ________

Name: ______________________________ Class: ___________Date: __________

Exercise 22.3 – Downburst Detection with Surface-based Anemometers

The Low-Level Windshear Alert System (LLWAS) is one method used near airports to detect downbursts. LLWAS consists of a network of closely spaced anemometers that are connected to a computer programmed to detect the spatial patterns of downburst winds.

An LLWAS network (labeled A – F), is shown surrounding a north-south airport runway. A circular downburst, with its center at the black dot on the left moves from left to right at a speed of 12 mph across the anemometer network between 1600 and 1630 local time. The downburst's diameter is 2 miles, and its *winds are radially outward at 40 mph at all points within the 4-mile diameter circle*. (This is an idealization, since the wind speeds of an actual downburst will vary across the downburst area.) Assume that winds in the background environment are calm and that 1 mph ≈ 1 knot.

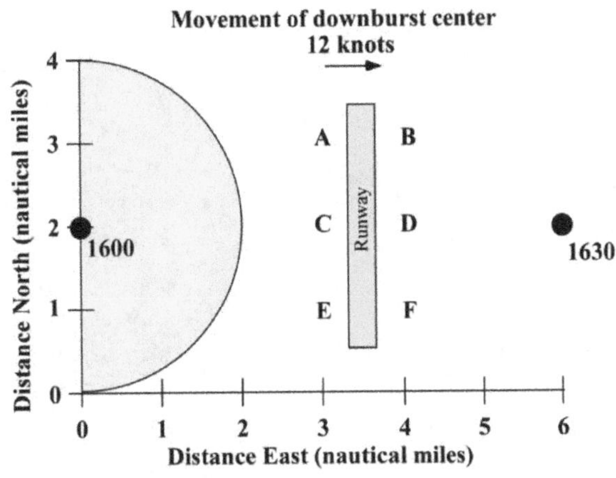

1. Using standard wind symbols (staffs and barbs), show how the winds varied between 1600 and 1630 local time at the different anemometers.

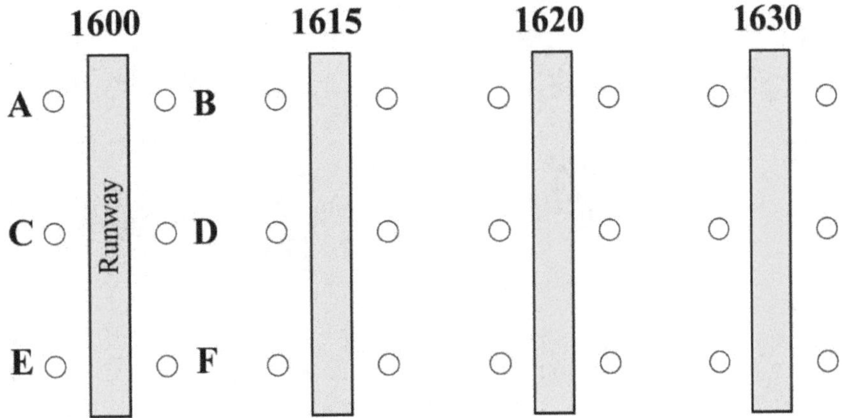

2. If the LLWAS software is designed to sound an alarm when the wind speed differs by 20 mph between any two anemometers, at what time should an LLWAS downburst alarm have sounded?

Name: ______________________________ Class: ___________Date: __________

Exercise 23.1 – Impacts of El Niño and La Niña

The table shows a summary of weather statistics during recent El Niño and La Niña years.

	Year	Winter (Nov-Mar) precipitation in San Francisco, CA	Total snowfall in Urbana, IL	Number of hurricanes in Atlantic Ocean
	Average	20″	26″	6
El Niño years	1982-1983	25″	15″	2
	1991-1992	12″	10″	4
	1997-1998	33″	12″	3
	2002-2003	23″	27″	4
	2004-2005	27″	13″	9
	2006-2007	15″	24″	5
	2009-2010	16″	27″	3
	2015-2016	21″	25″	4
	2018-2019	23″	13″	8
	2019-2020	10″	13″	6
La Niña years	1988-1989	12″	24″	5
	1995-1996	21″	38″	11
	1998-1999	15″	29″	10
	1999-2000	20″	20″	8
	2000-2001	17″	23″	8
	2007-2008	15″	26″	6
	2010-2011	23″	41″	12
	2011-2012	11″	11″	7
	2020-2021	9″	11″	14

1. Does there appear to be a relationship between winter precipitation in San Francisco and El Niño/La Niña years?

2. Does there appear to be a relationship between snowfall in Urbana, IL and El Niño/La Niña years?

3. What relationship appears to exist between hurricanes in the Atlantic Ocean and El Niño/La Niña years?

4. The actual precipitation amount (rain and snow together) in Urbana, Illinois during El Niño years is about average. Why would there be less snow?

5. During El Niño years, the polar and subtropical jetstreams are often in a different location compared to other years. How could this lead to the conditions shown above?

Name: ______________________________ Class: ___________Date: __________

Exercise 23.2 – ENSO and the Tropical Atmosphere and Ocean

Identify the statements as being either True (T) or False (F).

1. T F ENSO can persist for a season or longer, even up to a year, often resulting in a succession of unusual weather events.

2. T F The Walker Cell is a *north-south* circulation extending from the surface to the upper troposphere.

3. T F The term "Southern Oscillation" refers to the east-west seesaw of sea level pressure over the tropical Pacific Ocean.

4. T F Tahiti is normally dominated by low pressure at the surface.

5. T F During the El Niño phase of the Southern Oscillation, the normal upward vertical motion over Darwin is reduced in intensity.

6. T F The west-to-east winds in the tropics are known as the trade winds.

7. T F Upwelling normally occurs along the western coast of Peru and Ecuador.

8. T F Upwelling replaces ocean surface water with warmer water.

9. T F Upwelling is stronger during a La Niña than during an El Niño.

10. T F When the Walker Cell is stronger than normal, the trade winds are stronger than normal.

11. T F Ocean surface temperatures normally increase westward in the tropical Pacific Ocean because the trade winds blow from east to west.

12. T F When the Walker Cell weakens, the sea level pressure over Indonesia and northern Australia decreases.

13. T F In the trade wind region, the winds in the upper troposphere generally have an eastward component.

14. T F Winds near the equator are largely a response to the pressure gradient force because the Coriolis force is weak.

15. T F Frequency of El Niño events is forecast to increase significantly in the next century due to global climate change.

Name: ______________________________ Class: __________Date: __________

Exercise 23.3 – The Southern Oscillation Index (SOI)

The Southern Oscillation is based on the difference between the monthly sea level pressures at Tahiti in the central Pacific and Darwin, Australia. Specifically, the pressure's departure from normal at Darwin (PDN_{Darwin}) is subtracted from the pressure's departure from normal at Tahiti (PDN_{Tahiti}):

$$\text{Southern Oscillation Index} = PDN_{Tahiti} - PDN_{Darwin}$$

SOI values of -1 and +1 are generally regarded as the thresholds for El Niño and La Niña, respectively.

The table below contains actual values of the departures from normal pressure and/or values of the Southern Oscillation Index from various months during the past 20 years. In each case, fill in the missing value and indicate whether an El Niño or a La Niña (or neither) is occurring.

	PDN_{Tahiti}	PDN_{Darwin}	SOI	El Niño or La Niña?
January 1983	-3.3	+3.1		
July 1988	+1.3	-0.6		
January 1993		+0.1	-1.5	
June 1997		+1.8	-2.3	
November 1998	+0.3		+1.7	
January 2001	+2.4	+0.5		
November 2004	-0.9	-0.3		
October 2006		+2.1	-2.1	
January 2010	-2.8	-0.8		
December 2011	+2.2	-2.4		
February 2016	-1.9		-3.2	

Name: ______________________________ Class: ____________Date: __________

Exercise 24.1 – Hurricane Structure

The top diagram below is a cross-section of the clouds and circulations within a strong hurricane. The shaded areas represent the eyewall and spiral rainbands. In the lower portions of the diagram, draw a line that shows how the surface pressure, surface wind speed, rainfall rate, 700 mb temperature and storm surge height vary across the storm. Also, draw a line on the graph to the right of the cross-section to show how the wind speed varies with altitude in the eyewall. Assume the hurricane is moving into the page.

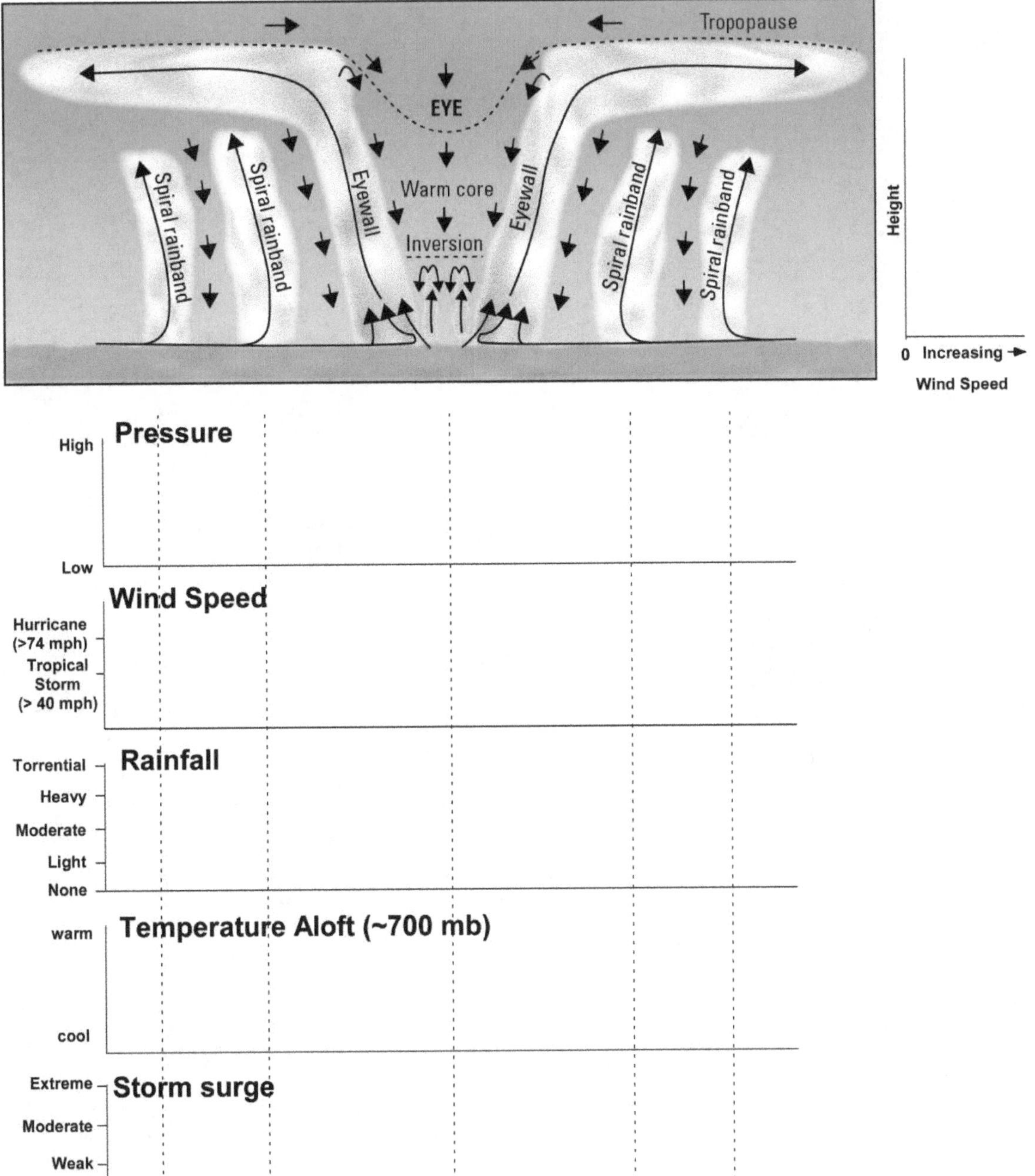

Name: ______________________________ Class: ___________Date: __________

Exercise 24.2 – Tropical Cyclone Winds and Saffir-Simpson Ratings

Wind speed is not constant across a tropical cyclone. Wind speed data (rotational wind speeds and forward movement) for four tropical cyclones is provided in the sketches. Four quadrants in each storm are defined relative to the direction the storm is moving. Use the information to evaluate the winds in the eyewall in the four quadrants of the storm (right, left, front and back). In addition, use the information provided to determine the Saffir-Simpson rating of each cyclone.

Abby

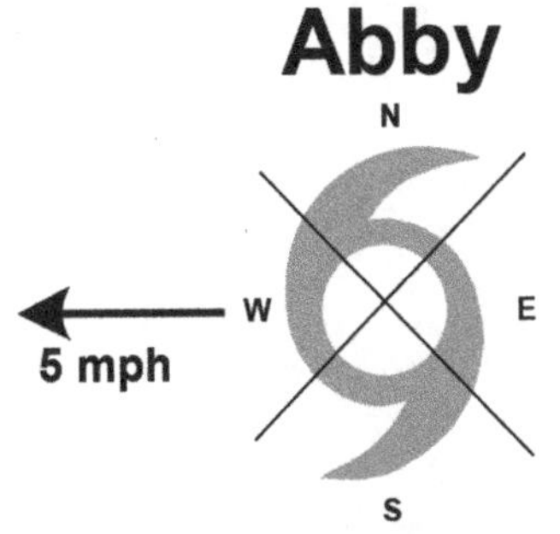

Rotational winds = 70 mph
Track: Westward at 5 mph

Benny

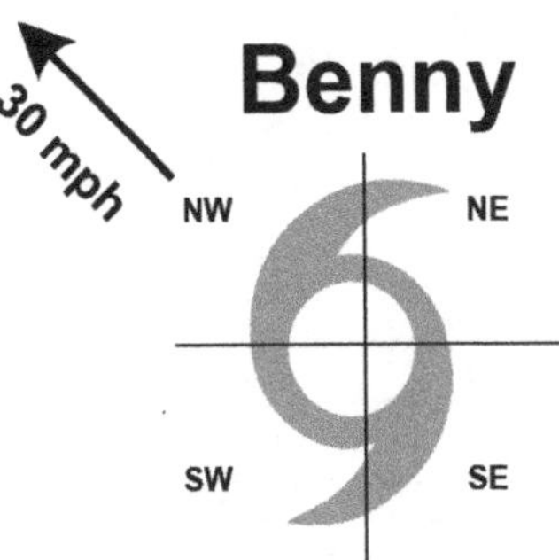

Rotational winds = 130 mph
Track: Northwestward at 30 mph

Carolyn

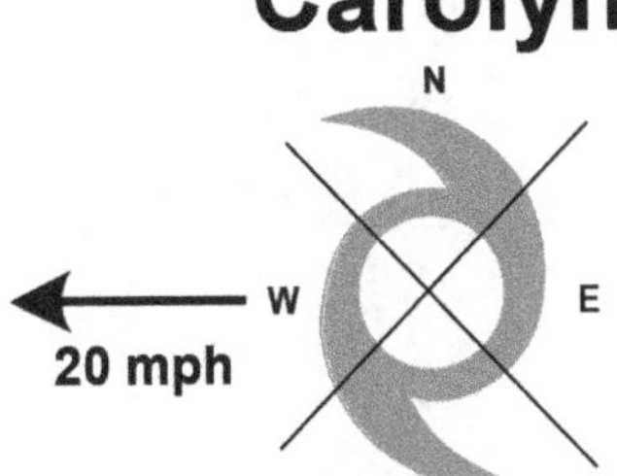

Rotational winds = 75 mph
Track: Westward at 20 mph
(in *Southern* Hemisphere)

Don

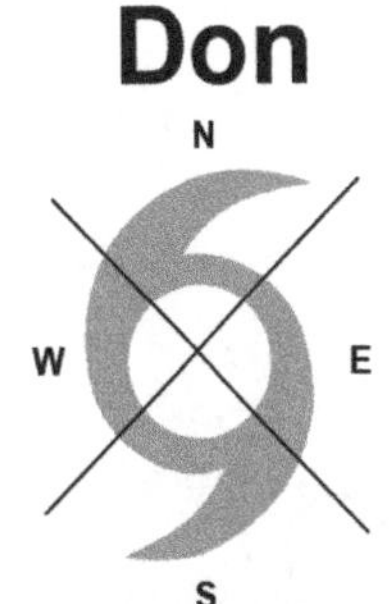

Rotational winds = 130 mph
Track: Stationary

	Wind in each quadrant				Saffir-Simpson rating
Hurricane Abby	N:	S:	E:	W:	
Hurricane Benny	NE:	SW:	NW:	SE:	
Cyclone Carolyn	N:	S:	E:	W:	
Hurricane Don	N:	S:	E:	W:	

Name: ______________________________ Class: ___________Date: _________

Exercise 24.3 – Tropical Cyclones: Physical and Dynamical Processes

Circle the word in parentheses that best captures the relationship. Then classify each as either:

(T) triggers of tropical thunderstorms,
(E) environmental requirements for tropical thunderstorms to organize into hurricanes, or
(I) intensification mechanisms.

1. ____ (Strong, Weak) vertical wind shear
2. ____ (Shallow, Deep) layer of warm water in the upper ocean
3. ____ Winds that (increase rapidly, do not change) with height
4. ____ Angular momentum (generation, dissipation, conservation)
5. ____ (Increase, Decrease) of surface pressure in the storm's center
6. ____ Location (more than, less than) five degrees from the equator
7. ____ Ocean surface temperatures (above, below) a threshold value
8. ____ (Absence, Presence) of Saharan air layers over the Atlantic Ocean.
9. ____ (Absence, Presence) of a strong jet stream just below the tropopause.
10. ____ Low-level (divergence, convergence) in an easterly wave in the trade winds
11. ____ Rising motion in the (Intertropical, Subtropical, Subpolar) Convergence Zone
12. ____ (Upwelling, sinking) of warm water allows hurricanes to (strengthen, weaken).
13. ____ Rotation of winds such that distance from axis of rotation (increases, decreases)
14. ____ (Pouch, Mesocyclone) within (easterly, westerly) waves protects core rotation area
15. ____ Wind-induced transfer of latent heat from (atmosphere, ocean) to (atmosphere, ocean)

Name: ______________________________ Class: ___________Date: _________

24.4 – Potential Hurricane Impacts at Landfall

The map below shows the Gulf Coast of Florida and a hurricane approaching land. The arrow denotes the direction of hurricane motion. Assuming the hurricane follows this path:

1. Which location(s) is(are) most vulnerable to storm surge? ______________________

2. Which location(s) will experience the heaviest rainfall? ______________________

3. Which location(s) will experience the strongest winds? ______________________

4. Explain how the forward speed of a hurricane impacts the amount of freshwater flooding experienced by locations inland, away from the coast.

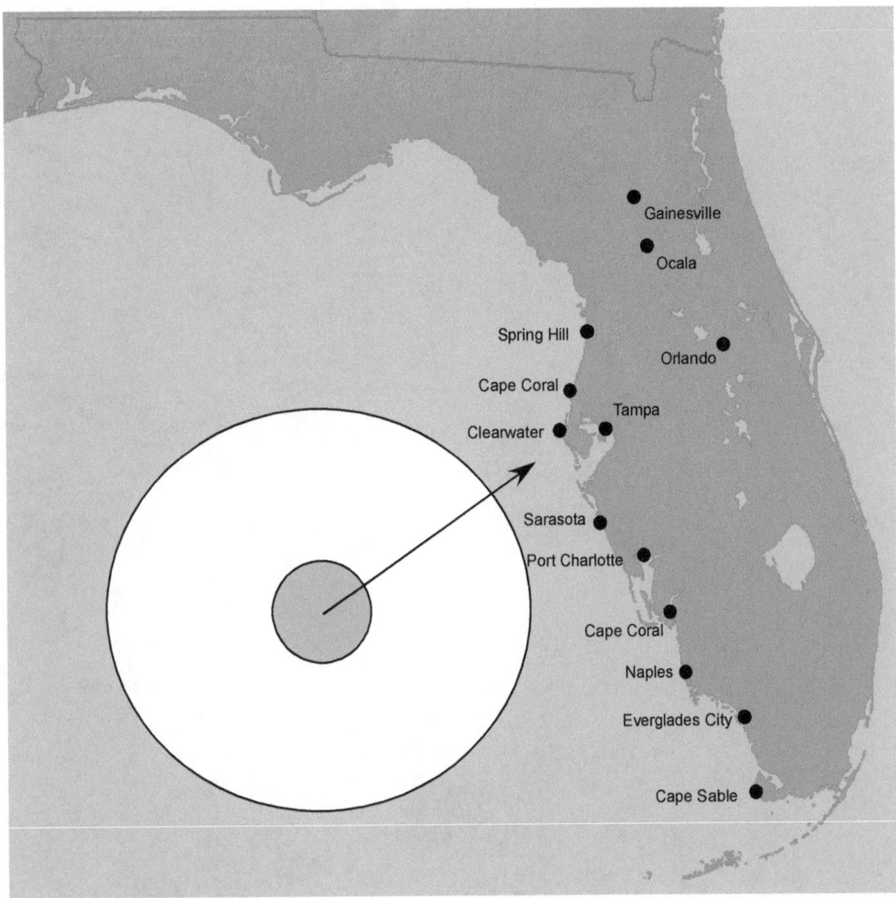

Name: ______________________________ Class: ___________Date: _________

Exercise 25.1 – Flood Types

Choose one of the following options that best fits each statement below.

Coastal flood

Widespread flood

Flash flood

1. _________ Most costly
2. _________ Most deadly
3. _________ Occurs on large rivers
4. _________ Occurs most often in July
5. _________ Often enhanced by snowmelt
6. _________ Associated with storm surge
7. _________ Localized, short-duration floods
8. _________ Occurs rapidly with little warning
9. _________ More frequent on small rivers and streams
10. _________ Common in the western mountain regions
11. _________ Covers a large area, often along a major river
12. _________ Often caused by slow-moving thunderstorms
13. _________ Develops slowly and tends to last a week or more
14. _________ Can be made worse if it occurs during a full moon
15. _________ Generally more extreme along the East and Gulf Coasts
16. _________ Primary source of these floods are slow-moving thunderstorms
17. _________ Occurs when a rise in the ocean surface develops due to storm surge
18. _________ Forms when a large amount of rain falls for many days over a watershed
19. _________ The time and day of the worst flooding is often predictable several days in advance

Name: ________________________________ Class: ___________Date: __________

Exercise 25.2 – Flood Locations and Timing

Complete the table below by selecting from the list the type of flood described.

Flash floods of desert southwest

Flash floods of eastern slope of Rocky Mountains

Flooding compounded by snowmelt

Frontal overrunning

Mesoscale Convective Systems (MCS) & frontal squall lines

Tropical cyclones

West Coast floods

Type of Flood	Time of Year	Possible areas Affected
	late winter and early spring	Canada and northern U.S.
	November through April	Georgia, Kentucky, Tennessee
	summer	Arizona, New Mexico
	winter	Oregon and California
	June through November	Coastal areas of eastern North America
	summer	Colorado, Wyoming
	late spring and summer	Canada and northern U.S.

Name: ______________________________ Class: ___________Date: _________

25.3 – Weather Phenomena and Floods

Seven weather phenomena associated with floods are listed below. Below the list are descriptions of floods taken from news reports. Match the report with the weather phenomenon that caused the flood described in the report. Each flood type is used once.

A. Tropical cyclone after landfall
B. Mesoscale convective system
C. Pineapple Express
D. Frontal overrunning
E. Squall Line
F. Thunderstorms over mountains
G. Floods enhanced by snowmelt

1. July 26: Three campers were killed today as a flash flood roared down a canyon in which they were camping and swept them into the rocks below the campground. Witnesses report the flood came out of "nowhere." Only light rain was reported at the campground at the base of the canyon, although lightning flashes and occasional distant thunder were observed the entire night just to the northeast. ____

2. November 30: Residents along the Little Sandy River in eastern Kentucky were forced from their homes after four days of steady cold rain caused the river to overflow its banks and flood homes along the river. After 15 inches of rain, insult was added to injury as snow fell on the beleaguered residents. ______

3. September 20: Torrential rain fell today in the eastern valleys of the Appalachian Mountains, causing very heavy flooding along both minor and major river systems. The rain was accompanied by buffeting winds, which felled trees and kept rescuers from reaching some remote areas that were particularly hard hit by flooding. ______

4. February 12: Over 30 inches of rain fell over 3 days in the mountains as southwesterly winds continued for yet another day. Reservoirs, unable to store the water, were forced to discharge it into the levee system. Several levees were topped and failed, causing three towns to fill with water to near their rooftops. ______

5. July 5: Extremely heavy rain accompanied by thunder and lightning ruined the July 4 celebration as storm drains filled to capacity and backed water into sewage systems. Forecasters initially expected the rain to move on, but the cold front stalled according to one forecaster, causing a "train" of thunderstorms to track over the city. ______

6. March 21: The flood is the result of a long winter, followed by heavy spring rains over western Pennsylvania and West Virginia. The crest on both the Allegheny and Monongahela rivers passed Pittsburgh last week and is now working its way down the Ohio River, where it is expected to pass Cincinnati in two days. ______

7. August 1: Extremely slow moving thunderstorms rumbled across western Iowa overnight. The storms continually regenerated over the same area for twelve hours, causing flooding along the Raccoon, Des Moines and Nishnabotna rivers. ______

Name: ______________________________ Class: ___________Date: _________

Exercise 25.4 – Flood Safety and Preparedness

Identify each statement about flood safety and preparedness as either being True (T) or False (F).

1. T F Six inches of water can sweep a person off their feet.

2. T F More than half of all people killed in floods are in vehicles.

3. T F It is more difficult to recognize the signs of flooding at night.

4. T F Not all factors affecting flood intensity are weather-related.

5. T F A levee protects a flood plain by decreasing a river's flow rate.

6. T F Coastal flooding occurs only in association with tropical cyclones.

7. T F If your vehicle stalls on a flooded roadway, do not abandon the vehicle.

8. T F Widespread floods are sometimes described as "leisurely disasters."

9. T F If your home is inundated by a 100-year flood in 2023, you can safely assume that a similar flood will not occur for the rest of the 21st century.

10. T F An automobile can be swept away by as little as eighteen inches of water.

11. T F Snowmelt is responsible for most flash floods that occur in the United States.

12. T F The skill of the National Weather Service in identifying potential flash flood events increased significantly in the 1990s as a result of the deployment of WSR-88D radars.

13. T F The National Weather Service issues a flash flood watch when a flash flood is occurring or imminent.

14. T F The actual amount of water that causes a 100-year flood varies from river to river and along a particular river.

15. T F Forecasting flash floods is not difficult because river conditions are monitored using streamflow gauges and water depth monitoring systems.

16. T F When a flood or flash flood warning is issued for your area, do not head for higher ground until an official personally comes to your house and tells you to evacuate.

Name: ______________________________ Class: __________ Date: _________

Exercise 26.1 – Types and Impacts of Drought

Several types of drought are distinguished on the basis of the impacts of a rainfall deficit. Examples of drought impacts are provided below. In each case, indicate whether the impact is best described as a manifestation of:

M: Meteorological drought (Lack of rainfall)
H: Hydrological drought (Reduced streamflow and reservoir capacity)
A: Agricultural drought (Drought reduces crop yield and impacts farming)
S: Socioeconomic drought (Financial losses to people and industries beyond farming)

1. _______ Local residential wells run dry.

2. _______ Barge traffic comes to a halt on the Mississippi River.

3. _______ Crop yield of farmers of the Great Plains is decreased.

4. _______ Streamflow rates drop to their lowest levels in 50 years.

5. _______ Reservoirs in California drop to 30 percent of capacity in April.

6. _______ Topsoil is picked up by the wind and blown across several states.

7. _______ Local water reservoirs are at less than half their maximum capacity.

8. _______ Snowfall for the season is only one third of typical amounts in Kansas.

9. _______ Rainfall for the spring season is less than 50 percent of normal over the Southern Plains.

10. _______ The price of future corn contracts on the Chicago Board of Trade rises to the maximum allowable amounts for five consecutive days in July.

11. _______ Thousands of residents are driven to migrate westward from the Plains after five years of drought.

12. _______ Ski-area operators in the western United States suffer through their worst year in a decade because of a deficient snow cover.

13. _______ Trees are severely stressed during a hot dry summer, resulting in the death of an abnormal percentage of trees over the next year.

14. _______ Foundations of buildings are damaged as the surrounding soil contracts and develops gaps due to the absence of moisture.

15. _______ Cities put a landscape watering-ban in place to allocate water resources for essential city services.

Name: ______________________________ Class: ____________Date: __________

Exercise 26.2 – Precipitation Deficits and Drought

The table below lists the normal seasonal precipitation amounts (inches) at four cities in the United States.

	Dec –Feb (winter)	Mar-May (spring)	Jun-Aug (summer)	Sep-Nov (autumn)	Year
A. Sacramento	9.2	4.4	0.1	2.5	16.2
B. Denver	1.9	6.0	4.5	3.1	15.5
C. St. Louis	6.1	10.7	10.6	8.5	35.9
D. Washington D.C.	8.3	10.5	11.6	10.8	41.2

1. Draw a line graph showing the seasonal cycle of precipitation at the four cities. Label the line graph for each city as A, B, C, or D.

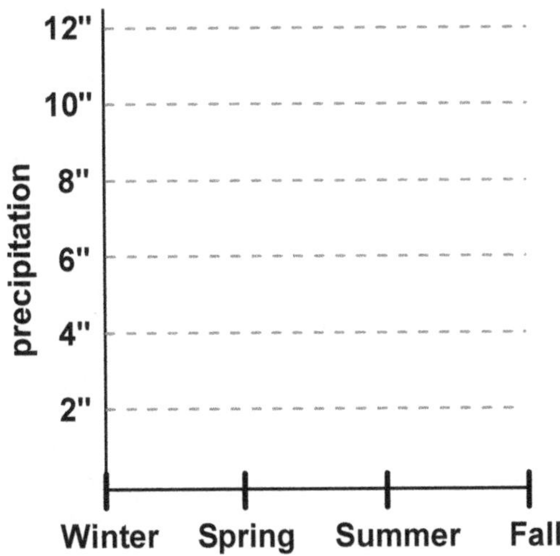

2. Which city would have the largest deficiency of precipitation (in inches) if a drought resulted in a 50 percent deficiency of precipitation in:

   winter? _________ spring? ________ summer? _________ fall?_________

3. Which city would lose the highest portion of its average annual precipitation if there were a 50% deficiency of precipitation in one season?

   ____

4. List two other factors that should also be considered in assessing the hydrological consequences of a deficit of precipitation.

   ____

   ____

Name: ______________________________ Class: ___________Date: _________

Exercise 26.3 – Understanding Drought

Identify each of the following as T (True) or F (False).

1. T F The mechanisms that initiate drought have been well established by meteorological research.

2. T F "Rain follows the plow."

3. T F The wintertime pattern of the jet stream is an important determinant of drought in the western United States.

4. T F Drought in the central United States is favored by a westward migration of the Bermuda high to a location near the Southeast Coast.

5. T F Soil moisture plays a role in the ability of a drought to perpetuate or "feed upon itself."

6. T F During a drought, days can be hotter than normal while nights are cooler than normal.

7. T F During a drought in the central United States, the jetstream is north of its normal position.

8. T F The central United States has never had a drought worse than that of the 1930s since agriculture became widespread in the late 1800s.

9. T F Extreme heat always accompanies a drought.

10. T F A closed high pressure center at 500 mb always precedes a drought in the United States.

11. T F The northeastern United States is immune to drought because of its proximity to the Gulf Stream.

12. T F There is no evidence that the settlement of the Great Plains by the European settlers had any impact on the intensity of meteorological drought.

13. T F El Niño is a robust predictor of drought in the central United States.

14. T F Current predictions of climate change are expected to increase both the frequency and severity of drought in the United States.

15. T F Climate models suggest that the levels of aridity of the Dust Bowl and the 1950s drought could become the new norm for the southwestern United States.

16. T F Droughts are not associated with persistent departures of large-scale weather patterns, rather are driven by local influences such as topography and microclimates.

Name: ______________________________ Class: ___________Date: __________

Exercise 26.4 – Drought Weather Patterns Aloft

On each of the three maps below, draw a 700 mb height pattern that would eventually lead to drought conditions in the indicated region if the pattern persisted for several months.

DROUGHT IN MID-ATLANTIC STATES

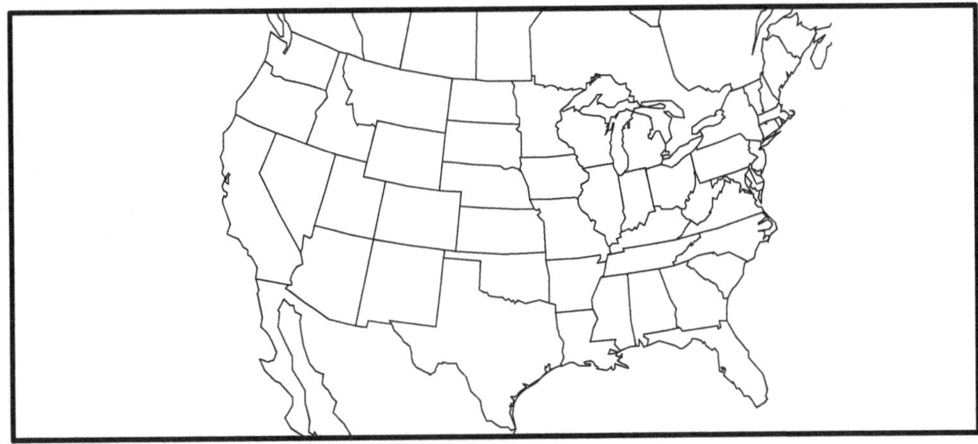

DROUGHT IN CENTRAL U.S.

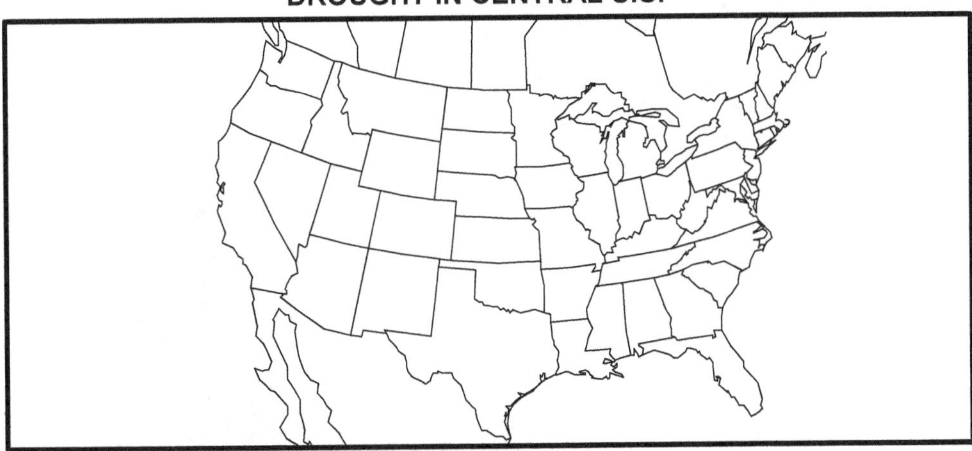

DROUGHT IN WESTERN MOUNTAIN STATES

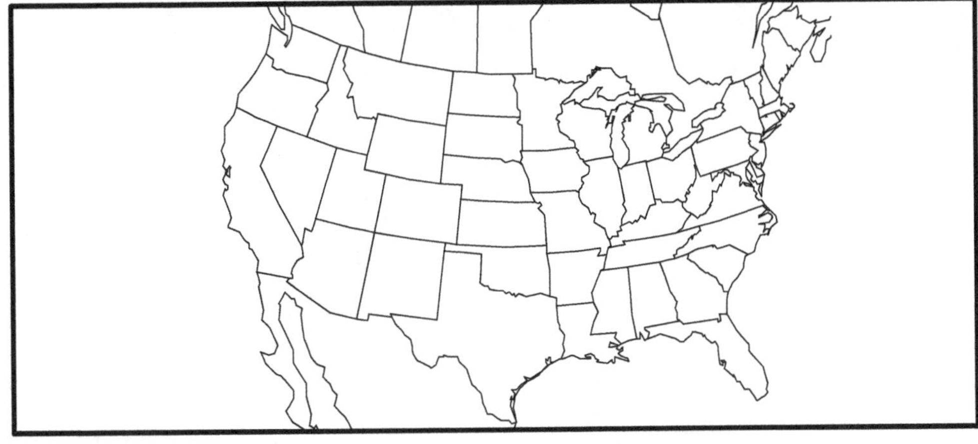

Name: ______________________________ Class: ___________Date: __________

Exercise 27.1 – Heat Index Calculations

The surface reports below were obtained from stations affected by a summer heat wave. In each case, estimate the Heat Index using the chart provided. Additionally, indicate whether the wind will have a warming effect or a cooling effect on a person wearing light clothing.

City	Temperature	Relative Humidity	Wind	Heat Index	Effect of wind (warming/cooling/none)
1. Chicago, IL	90°F	55%	10 mph		
2. Pheonix, AZ	103°F	45%	20 mph		
3. Boston, MA	86°F	75%	calm		
4. Santa Fe, NM	80°F	45%	5 mph		
5. Raleigh, NC	94°F	70%	15 mph		
6. New York City, NY	94°F	60%	15 mph		
7. Pittsburgh, PA	94°F	50%	15 mph		
8. Miami, FL	94°F	80%	15 mph		
9. Minneapolis, MN	82°F	95%	calm		
10. Los Angeles, CA	88°F	40%	5 mph		

HEAT INDEX AS A FUNCTION OF TEMPERATURE AND RELATIVE HUMIDITY

Relative Humidity (%)

Air Temp. (°F)	40	45	50	55	60	65	70	75	80	85	90	95	100
110	138												
108	130	137											
106	124	130	137										
104	119	124	131	137									
102	114	119	124	130	137								
100	109	114	118	124	129	130							
98	105	109	113	117	123	128	134						
96	101	104	108	112	116	121	126	132					
94	97	100	102	106	110	114	119	124	129	136			
92	94	96	99	101	105	108	112	116	121	126	131		
90	91	93	95	97	100	103	106	109	113	117	122	127	132
88	88	89	91	93	95	98	100	103	106	110	113	117	121
86	85	87	88	89	91	93	95	97	100	102	105	108	112
84	83	84	85	86	88	89	90	92	94	96	98	100	103
82	81	82	83	84	84	95	86	88	89	90	91	93	95
80	80	80	81	81	82	82	84	84	84	85	86	86	87

Name: ______________________________ Class: ___________Date: __________

Exercise 27.2 – Inversions and Surface Heating

Inversions are very stable layers of air. By preventing the mixing of humid air near the surface and drier air aloft, inversions can enhance the build-up of humidity and heat indices near the surface. Fill in the blanks for each of the soundings shown below. Note that the soundings only show the lowest 5 km of the troposphere.

	SOUNDING A	SOUNDING B
(a) Surface air temperature	________	________
(b) height at base of inversion	________	________
(c) height at top of inversion	________	________
(d) temperature at top of inversion	________	________
(e) temperature at base of inversion	________	________
(f) magnitude of inversion ($T_{top} - T_{bottom}$)	________	________
(g) surface air temperature required to eliminate inversion	________	________

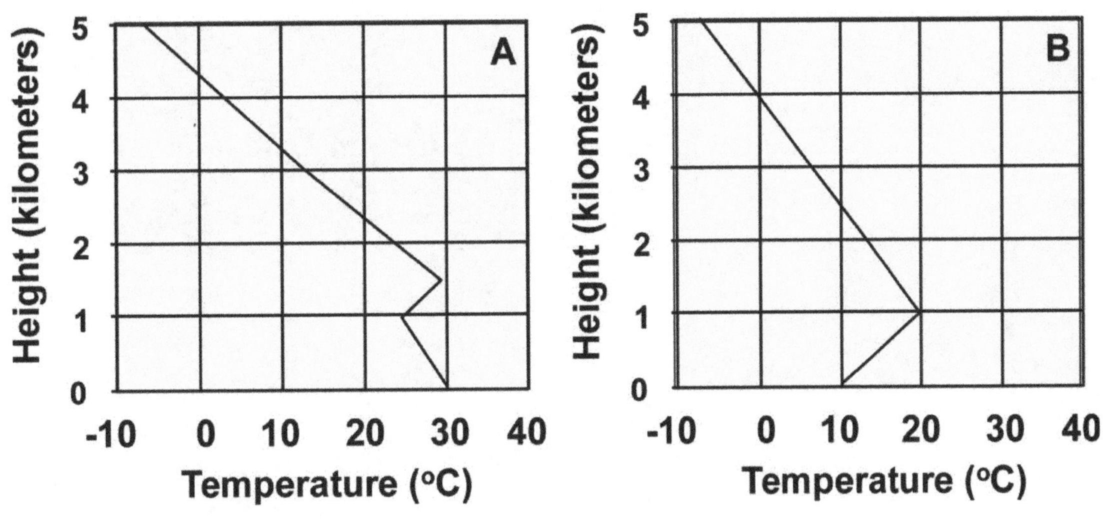

Name: ______________________________ Class: __________Date: _________

Exercise 27.3 – Meteorology of Heat Waves

Circle the correct answers to indicate how each of the factors below affects a heat wave and the various measures of heat severity.

1. Temperature and (cloud cover; humidity) are the most important determinants of heat stress and human discomfort.
2. Evaporation from a wet surface will (increase; decrease; not affect) the Heat Index.
3. Daytime cloud cover will (increase; decrease; not affect) the apparent temperature.
4. Northward migration of the jetstream will (increase; decrease; not affect) the likelihood of a heat wave.
5. An intensifying surface high 500 miles to the west of a location will (increase; decrease; not affect) the likelihood of a heat wave at that location.
6. Westerly winds along the East Coast during the summer (increase; decrease; do not affect) the likelihood of an East Coast heat wave.
7. Westerly winds along the West Coast during the summer (increase; decrease; do not affect) the likelihood of a West Coast heat wave.
8. A large or "steep" environmental lapse rate favors (high; low) humidities at the surface during a heat wave.
9. Nighttime minimum temperatures during a heat wave can be expected to be highest when the overlying airmass is (continental Polar; continental Tropical).
10. Surface high pressure centers are most often found to the (east; west) of areas affected by heat waves.
11. A persistent heat wave is often associated with a closed (high; low) pressure center at the 700 mb level.
12. The vertical motions in the middle troposphere above an area affected by a heat wave are generally (upward; downward).
13. The drier the ground, the (more; less) solar energy is used for heating the ground and the air near the ground.
14. During a heat wave, the temperature difference between urban and rural areas is generally greatest (late at night; late in the afternoon).
15. Wind is an effective (cooling; warming) agent as long as the air temperature is less than the body skin temperature.

Name: ________________________________ Class: ____________Date: __________

Exercise 27.4 – Urban Heat Island

The figure below shows a cross section through an urban area. The temperature values listed are measured values at each of the locations shown on the diagram, but not in the same left-to-right sequence as the locations on the diagram. Plot the temperatures in the appropriate location to show how air temperature varies across rural and urban areas.

Measured Air Temperatures

84°F
86°F
87°F
88°F
88°F
92°F

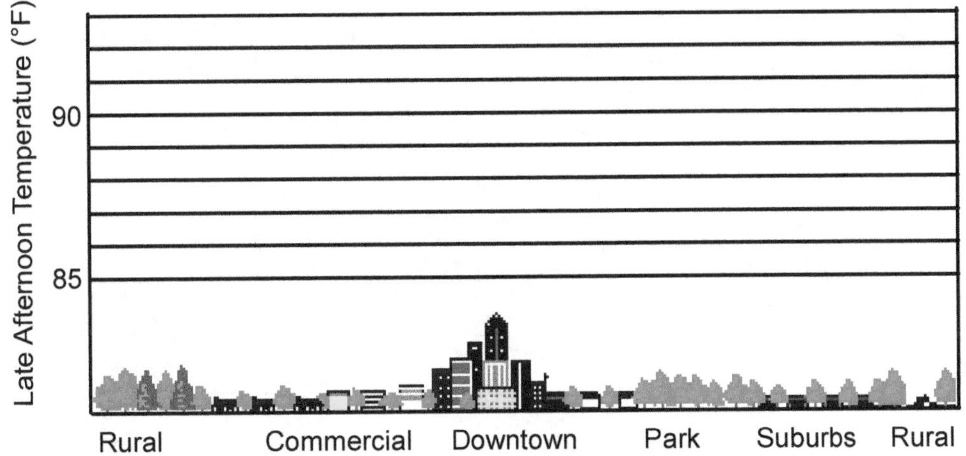

Briefly explain why you chose the temperature distribution that you did. Your explanation should include some of the factors that influence the urban heat island.

Name: ______________________________ Class: ___________Date: _________

Exercise 28.1 – Prescribed Burn

You are employed by a fire management agency in central Kansas, and are charged with carrying out a prescribed burn as part of a prairie restoration activity. The burn must occur during a one-week period, during which additional firefighters will be available to ensure that the fire does not burn out of control. Based on past experience with prescribed burns of the same area, the time required for the burn is approximately six hours.

The following is the weather forecast for the week in which the burn is to occur.

Day 1: Increasing clouds, highs in the 50s, winds SW at 10-15 mph, Relative Humidity (RH) 50-60%

Day 2: Showers and thunderstorms likely, highs in the 60s, winds SW at 20 mph, RH 60-70%

Day 3: Clearing, highs in the 40s, winds NW at 10-20 mph, RH 30-40%

Day 4: Sunny, breezy, highs in the 50s, winds NW at 10-20 mph, RH 30-40%

Day 5: Partly cloudy, highs in the 60s, winds SW at 5-10 mph, RH 40-50%:

Day 6: Cloudy, highs in the 70s, winds S at 10-15 mph, RH 70-80%

Day 7: Cloudy, showers possible, highs in the 60s, winds SE at 15-20 mph, RH 90%

1. Which day would you choose for the prescribed burn? ____________

2. Provide a justification for your choice of this day for the burn.

   ____

3. Which time of day would you choose for the start of the burn? ____________

4. Explain why you choose this time of day for the start of the fire.

   ____

5. What time of year do you think would be best for a prescribed burn of a prairie in Kansas? Why?

   ____

Name: ______________________________ Class: ___________Date: __________

Exercise 28.2 – Wildfire Trends

Wildfire activity in Alaska is highly variable from year to year. Climate assessments have pointed to increases in wildfire activity. The graph shows the number of acres burned annually over a 70-year period, 1950-2019, with the first bar being 1950. Years with no fires have no bars. Years with more than one million acres burned are colored orange.

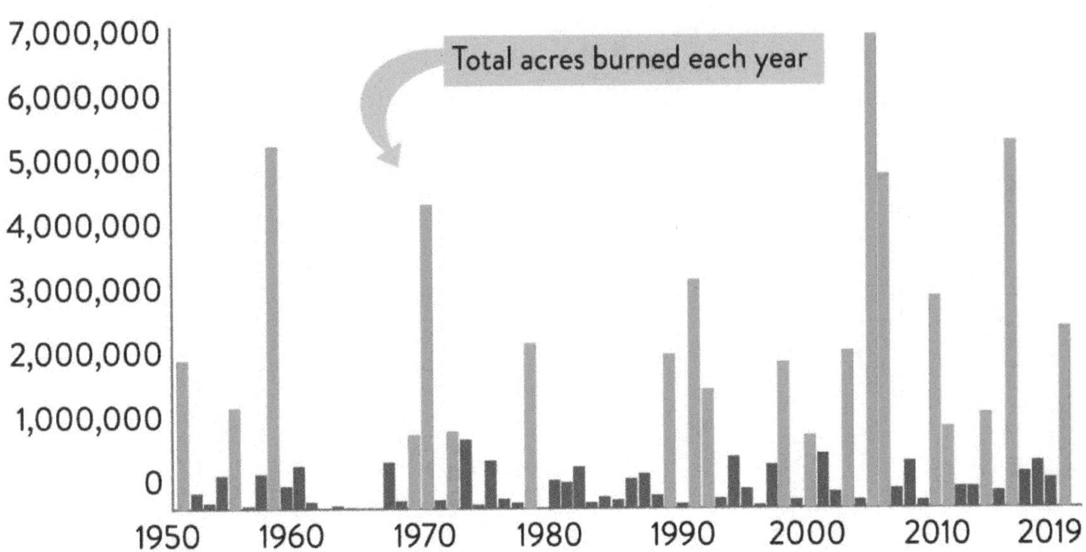

1. The five years individual years with the most acres burned: _____________

2. Number of million-acre burn years in first half of period (1950-1984): _____________

3. Number of million-acre burn years in second half of period (1985-2019):

    ____

4. If you were asked whether there is compelling evidence for increased wildfire activity in Alaska, how would you answer?

    ____

    ____

Name: ______________________________ Class: ____________Date: __________

Exercise 28.3 – Wildfires in the Western U.S.

The following table shows the approximate numbers of acres burned by wildfires in several western states during the years 2017 through 2020:

	California	Oregon	Montana	Colorado
2020	4,200,000	1,100,000	380,000	660,000
2019	260,000	80,000	65,000	40,000
2018	1,670,000	90,000	98,000	460,000
2017	1,250,000	60,000	1,400,000	110,000

Below are the U.S. Drought Monitor maps for August 31 of each of these years, with the years, randomly arranged. Using the state burn areas as a guide, identify the year of each map by filling in the blanks below the maps.

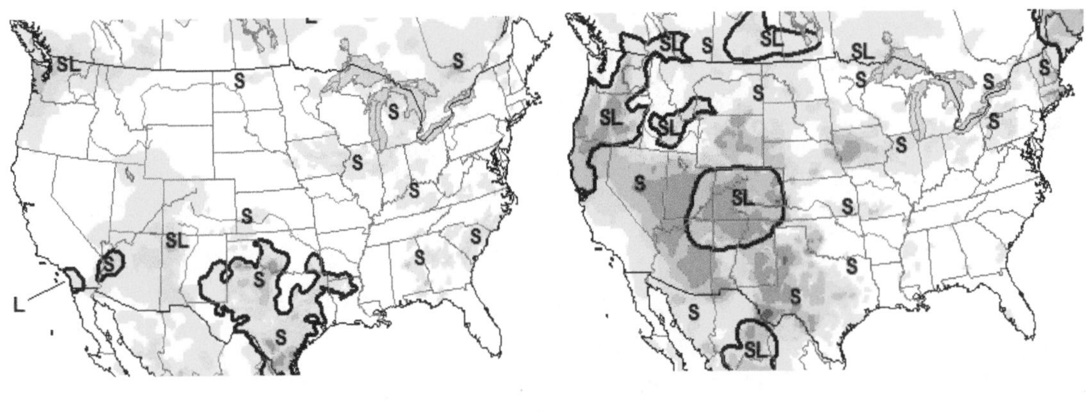

__________ __________

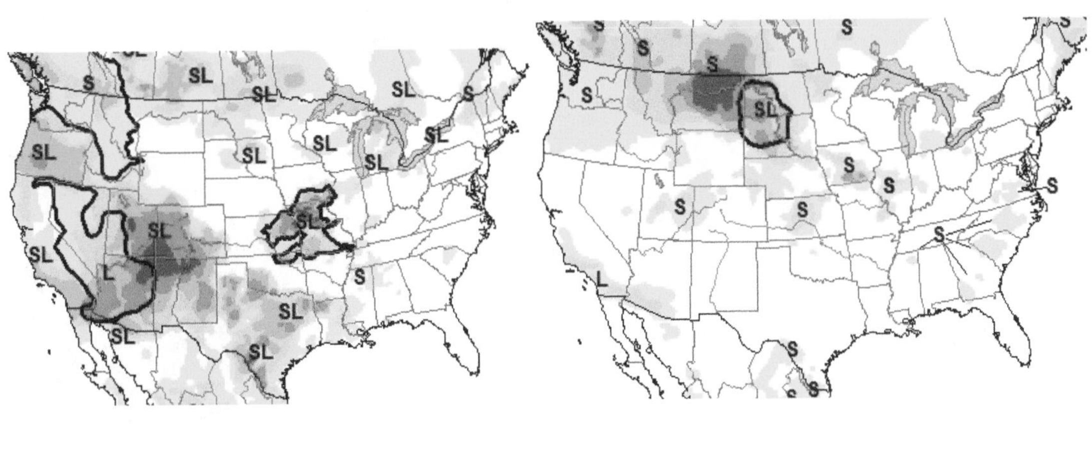

__________ __________

CPSIA information can be obtained
at www.ICGtesting.com
Printed in the USA
LVHW060903180222
710696LV00004B/1

9 781792 462832